BIOZONE

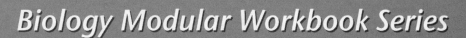

Biology Modular Workbook Series

Health & Disease

Authors

Tracey Greenwood

Lyn Shepherd

Richard Allan

Artwork by Daniel Butler

PUBLISHED BY:

Biozone International Ltd
P.O. Box 13-034, Hamilton, New Zealand
Telephone: +64(7)856 8104
Fax: +64(7)856 9243
FREEFAX: 1-800717-8751 (USA-Canada only)
Email: sales@biozone.co.nz

UNITED KINGDOM
Biozone Learning Media (UK) Ltd
P.O. Box 23698, Edinburgh EH5 2WX, Scotland
Telephone: (131)557 5060
Fax: (131)557 5030
Email: sales@biozone.co.uk

© 2006 **Biozone International Ltd**
Printed by REPLIKA PRESS PVT LTD

ISBN: 1-877329-74-6 paperback

Front cover photographs:

Stethoscopes. Image ©2005 JupiterImages Corporation www.clipart.com

Patient examination. Image ©1996 Digital Stock Corporation (Medicine & Healthcare collection)

Biology Modular Workbook Series

The Biozone *Biology Modular Workbook Series* has been developed to meet the demands of customers with the requirement for a modular resource which can be used in a flexible way. Like Biozone's popular Student Resource and Activity Manuals, these workbooks provide a collection of visually interesting and accessible activities, which cater for students with a wide range of abilities and background. The workbooks are divided into a series of chapters, each comprising an introductory section with detailed learning objectives and useful resources, and a series of write-on activities ranging from paper practicals and data handling exercises, to questions requiring short essay style answers. Material for these workbooks has been drawn from Biozone's popular, widely used manuals, but the workbooks have been structured with greater ease of use and flexibility in mind. During the development of this series, we have taken the opportunity to improve the design and content, while retaining the basic philosophy of a student-friendly resource which spans the gulf between textbook and study guide. With its unique, highly visual presentation, it is possible to engage and challenge students, increase their motivation and empower them to take control of their learning.

Health & Disease

This title in the *Biology Modular Workbook Series* provides students with a set of comprehensive guidelines and highly visual worksheets through which to explore aspects of human health and disease and the role of modern medicine in treating and preventing health disorders. *Health & Disease* is the ideal companion for students of the life sciences, encompassing not only infectious and non-infectious disease, but the nature of immunity, immune system dysfunction, preventative and diagnostic techniques, and treatments for disease. This workbook comprises four chapters, each covering a different aspect of human health. These areas are explained through a series of one and two page activities, each of which explores a specific concept (e.g. cancer or malaria). Model answers (on CD-ROM) accompany each order free of charge. *Health & Disease* is a student-centred resource. Students completing the activities, in concert with their other classroom and practical work, will consolidate existing knowledge and develop and practise skills that they will use throughout their course. This workbook may be used in the classroom or at home as a supplement to a standard textbook. Some activities are introductory in nature, while others may be used to consolidate and test concepts already covered by other means. Biozone has a commitment to produce a cost-effective, high quality resource, which acts as a student's companion throughout their biology study. Please do not photocopy from this workbook; we cannot afford to provide single copies of workbooks to schools and continue to develop, update, and improve the material they contain.

Acknowledgements and Photo Credits

• Joan and John Allan for kindly agreeing to pose for the photos on age related health issues • Joseph E. Armstrong, Professor of Botany, Head Curator at ISU Herbarium, USA for his permission to use the photo showing a child with kwashiorkor • Bio-Rad Laboratories, Inc. for allowing us to photograph the Helios gene gun• Hemosol Inc. for use of their photograph in the blood substitutes activity • Sue Fitzgerald and Mary McDougall for their efficient handling of the office • Dr. Nita Scobie, Cytogenetics Department, Waikato Hospital for chromosome photos • Genesis Research and Development Corp. Auckland, for the photo used on the HGP activity • ©1999 University of Kansas, for the photo of the incubator for culture of cell lines • Charles Goldberg, University of California, San Diego School of Medicine, for the photograph of a patient with rheumatoid arthritis • Totem Graphics, for their clipart collection of plants and animals • TechPool Studios, for their fabulous clipart collection of human anatomy: Copyright ©1994, TechPool Studios Corp. USA (some images were modified by R. Allan and T. Greenwood) • Corel Corporation, for clipart of plants and animals from the Corel MEGAGALLERY collection • 3D models created using Poser IV, Curious Labs.Photos kindly provided by individuals or corporations have been indentified by way of coded credits as follows: **CDC**: Centers for Disease Control and Prevention, Atlanta, USA, **EII**: Education Interactive Imaging, **Eyewire**: Eyewire Inc © 1998-2001, www.eyewire.com, **HGSI**: Dena Borchardt at Human Genome Sciences Inc., **NICD**: National Institute on Chemical Dependency, **RA**: Richard Allan

Also in this series:

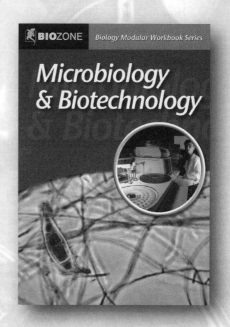

Microbiology & Biotechnology

ISBN: 1-877329-73-8

Skills in Biology

ISBN: 1-877329-71-1 (UK edition)

ISBN: 1-877329-72-X (International edition)

Contents

Activity is marked: ☐ to be done; ✓ when completed

How to Use this Workbook

Health & Disease is designed to provide students with a resource that will make the acquisition of knowledge and skills in this area easier and more enjoyable. The study of disease, its role in human societies, and its prevention and treatment are important in many biology curricula. Moreover, this subject is of high interest, being topical, rapidly changing, and highly relevant to students in their everyday life. This workbook is suitable for all students of the life sciences, and will reinforce and extend the ideas developed by teachers. It is **not a textbook**; its aim is to complement the texts written for your particular course. *Health & Disease* provides the following resources in each chapter. You should refer back to them as you work through each set of worksheets.

Guidance Provided for Each Topic

Learning objectives

These provide you with a map of the chapter content. Completing the learning objectives relevant to your course will help you to satisfy the knowledge requirements of your syllabus. Your teacher may decide to leave out points or add to this list.

Chapter content

The upper panel of the header identifies the general content of the chapter. The lower panel provides a brief summary of the chapter content.

Key words

Key words are displayed in **bold** type in the learning objectives and should be used to create a glossary as you study each topic. From your teacher's descriptions and your own reading, write your own definition for each word.

Note: Only the terms relevant to your selected learning objectives should be used to create your glossary. Free glossary worksheets are also available from our web site

Use the check boxes to mark objectives to be completed.
Use a **dot** to be done (•).
Use a **tick** when completed (✓).

Supplementary texts

References to supplementary texts suitable for use with this workbook are provided. Chapter references are provided as appropriate. The details of these are provided on page 7, together with other resources information.

Supplementary resources

Biozone's Presentation MEDIA are noted where appropriate

Periodical articles

Ideal for those seeking more depth or the latest research on a specific topic. Articles are sorted according to their suitability for student or teacher reference. Visit your school, public, or university library for these articles

Internet addresses:

Access our database of links to more than **800** web sites (updated regularly) relevant to the topics covered. Go to Biozone's own web site: **www.thebiozone.com** and link directly to listed sites using the *BioLinks* button.

Activity Pages

The activities and exercises make up most of the content of this workbook. They are designed to reinforce the concepts you have learned about in the topic. Your teacher may use the activity pages to introduce a topic for the first time, or you may use them to revise ideas already covered. They are excellent for use in the classroom, and as homework exercises and revision. In most cases, the activities should not be attempted until you have carried out the necessary background reading from your textbook. As a self-check, model answers for each activity are provided on CD-ROM with each order of workbooks.

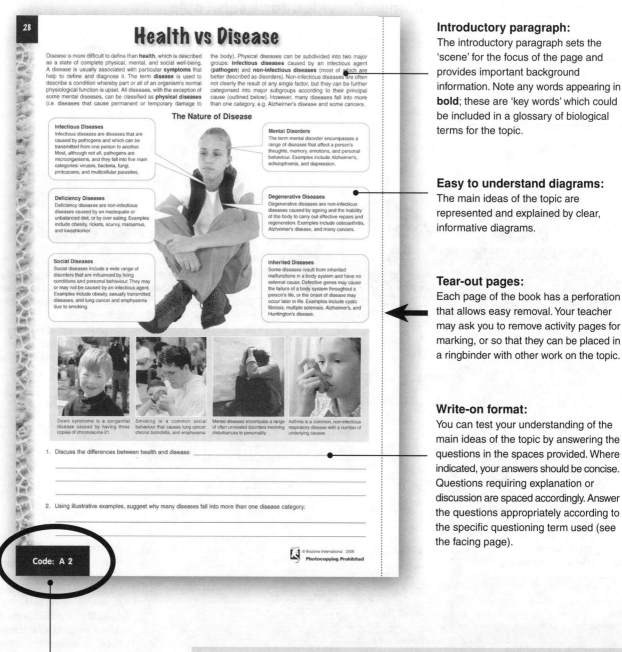

Introductory paragraph:
The introductory paragraph sets the 'scene' for the focus of the page and provides important background information. Note any words appearing in **bold**; these are 'key words' which could be included in a glossary of biological terms for the topic.

Easy to understand diagrams:
The main ideas of the topic are represented and explained by clear, informative diagrams.

Tear-out pages:
Each page of the book has a perforation that allows easy removal. Your teacher may ask you to remove activity pages for marking, or so that they can be placed in a ringbinder with other work on the topic.

Write-on format:
You can test your understanding of the main ideas of the topic by answering the questions in the spaces provided. Where indicated, your answers should be concise. Questions requiring explanation or discussion are spaced accordingly. Answer the questions appropriately according to the specific questioning term used (see the facing page).

Activity code:
Activities are coded to help you in identifying the type of activities and the skills they require. Most activities require some basic knowledge recall, but will usually build on this to include applying the knowledge to explain observations or predict outcomes. The least difficult questions generally occur early in the activity, with more challenging questions towards the end of the activity.

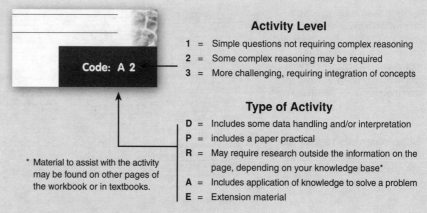

* Material to assist with the activity may be found on other pages of the workbook or in textbooks.

Activity Level

1 = Simple questions not requiring complex reasoning
2 = Some complex reasoning may be required
3 = More challenging, requiring integration of concepts

Type of Activity

D = Includes some data handling and/or interpretation
P = includes a paper practical
R = May require research outside the information on the page, depending on your knowledge base*
A = Includes application of knowledge to solve a problem
E = Extension material

Explanation of Terms

Questions come in a variety of forms. Whether you are studying for an exam or writing an essay, it is important to understand exactly what the question is asking. A question has two parts to it: one part of the question will provide you with information, the second part of the question will provide you with instructions as to how to answer the question. Following these instructions is most important. Often students in examinations know the material but fail to follow instructions and do not answer the question appropriately. Examiners often use certain key words to introduce questions. Look out for them and be clear as to what they mean. Below is a description of terms commonly used when asking questions in biology.

Commonly used Terms in Biology

The following terms are frequently used when asking questions in examinations and assessments. Students should have a clear understanding of each of the following terms and use this understanding to answer questions appropriately.

Account for: Provide a satisfactory explanation or reason for an observation.

Analyse: Interpret data to reach stated conclusions.

Annotate: Add **brief** notes to a diagram, drawing or graph.

Apply: Use an idea, equation, principle, theory, or law in a new situation.

Appreciate: To understand the meaning or relevance of a particular situation.

Calculate: Find an answer using mathematical methods. Show the working unless instructed not to.

Compare: Give an account of similarities and differences between two or more items, referring to both (or all) of them throughout. Comparisons can be given using a table. Comparisons generally ask for similarities more than differences (see contrast).

Construct: Represent or develop in graphical form.

Contrast: Show differences. Set in opposition.

Deduce: Reach a conclusion from information given.

Define: Give the precise meaning of a word or phrase as concisely as possible.

Derive: Manipulate a mathematical equation to give a new equation or result.

Describe: Give a detailed account, including all the relevant information.

Design: Produce a plan, object, simulation or model.

Determine: Find the only possible answer.

Discuss: Give an account including, where possible, a range of arguments, assessments of the relative importance of various factors, or comparison of alternative hypotheses.

Distinguish: Give the difference(s) between two or more different items.

Draw: Represent by means of pencil lines. Add labels unless told not to do so.

Estimate: Find an approximate value for an unknown quantity, based on the information provided and application of scientific knowledge.

Evaluate: Assess the implications and limitations.

Explain: Give a clear account including causes, reasons, or mechanisms.

Identify: Find an answer from a number of possibilities.

Illustrate: Give concrete examples. Explain clearly by using comparisons or examples.

Interpret: Comment upon, give examples, describe relationships. Describe, then evaluate.

List: Give a sequence of names or other brief answers with no elaboration. Each one should be clearly distinguishable from the others.

Measure: Find a value for a quantity.

Outline: Give a brief account or summary. Include essential information only.

Predict: Give an expected result.

Solve: Obtain an answer using algebraic and/or numerical methods.

State: Give a specific name, value, or other answer. No supporting argument or calculation is necessary.

Suggest: Propose a hypothesis or other possible explanation.

Summarise: Give a brief, condensed account. Include conclusions and avoid unnecessary details.

In Conclusion

Students should familiarise themselves with this list of terms and, where necessary throughout the course, they should refer back to them when answering questions. The list of terms mentioned above is not exhaustive and students should compare this list with past examination papers / essays etc. and add any new terms (and their meaning) to the list above. The aim is to become familiar with interpreting the question and answering it appropriately.

Using the Internet

The internet is a vast global network of computers connected by a system that allows information to be passed through telephone connections. When people talk about the internet they usually mean the **World Wide Web** (WWW). The WWW is a service that has made the internet so simple to use that virtually anyone can find their way around, exchange messages, search libraries and perform all manner of tasks. The internet is a powerful resource for locating information. Listed below are two journal articles worth reading. They contain useful information on what the internet is, how to get started, examples of useful web sites, and how to search the internet.

- **Click Here: Biology on the Internet** Biol. Sci. Rev., 10(2) November 1997, pp. 26-29.
- **An A-level biologists guide to The World Wide Web** Biol. Sci. Rev., 10(4) March 1998, pp. 26-29.

Using the Biozone Website: www.thebiozone.com

The **Back** and **Forward** buttons allow you to navigate between pages displayed on a www site

The current **internet address (URL)** or the web site is displayed here. You can type in a new address directly into this space

Tool bar provides a row of buttons with shortcuts for some commonly performed tasks, such as printing a page or 'refreshing' the page (i.e. making the page load again).

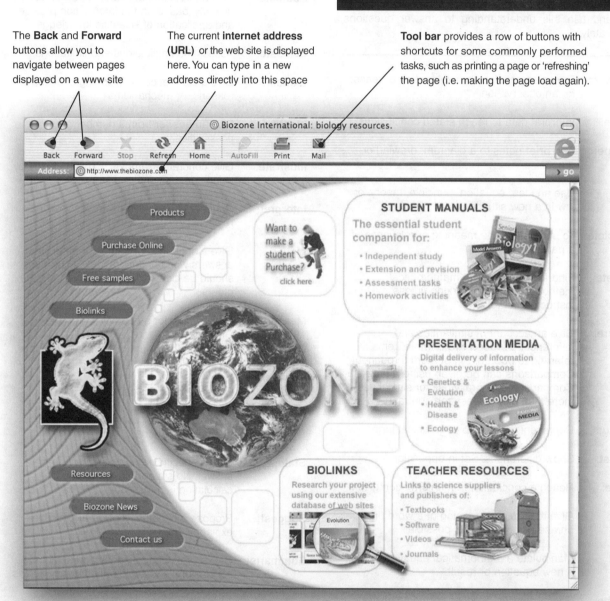

Searching the Net

The WWW addresses listed throughout the manual have been selected for their relevance to the topic in which they are listed. We believe they are good sites. Don't just rely on the sites that we have listed. Use the powerful 'search engines', which can scan the millions of sites for useful information. Here are some good ones to try:

Alta Vista:	**www.altavista.com**
Ask Jeeves:	**www.ask.com**
Excite:	**www.excite.com/search**
Google:	**www.google.com**
Go.com:	**www.go.com**
Lycos:	**www.lycos.com**
Metacrawler:	**www.metacrawler.com**
Yahoo:	**www.yahoo.com**

 © Biozone International 2006

Biozone International provides a service on its web site that links to all internet sites listed in this workbook. Our web site also provides regular updates with new sites listed as they come to our notice and defunct sites deleted. Our **BIO LINKS** page shown below, will take you to a database of regularly updated links to more than 800 other quality biology web sites

The **Resource Hub**, accessed via the homepage or resources, provides links to the supporting resources referenced in the workbook. These resources include comprehensive and supplementary texts, biology dictionaries computer software, videos, and science supplies. These can be used to enhance your learning experience.

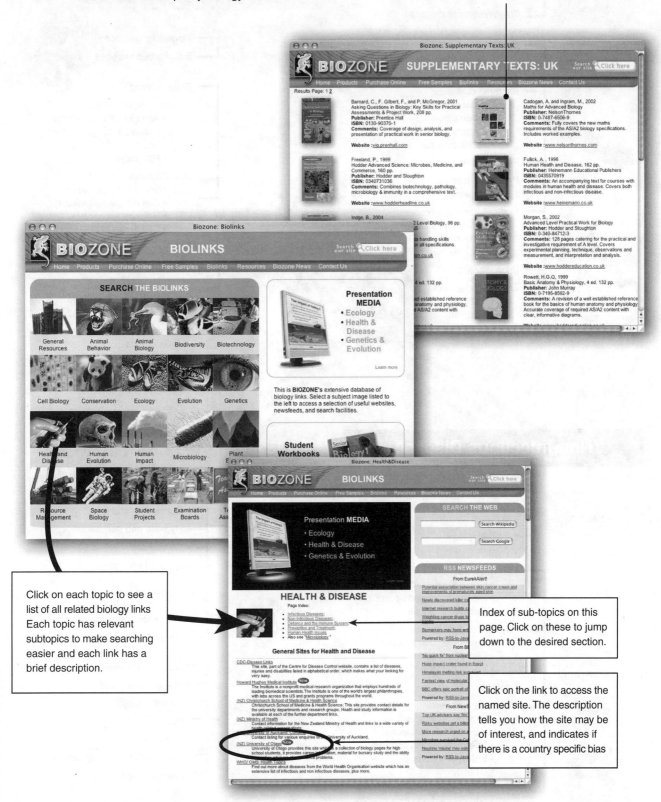

Click on each topic to see a list of all related biology links Each topic has relevant subtopics to make searching easier and each link has a brief description.

Index of sub-topics on this page. Click on these to jump down to the desired section.

Click on the link to access the named site. The description tells you how the site may be of interest, and indicates if there is a country specific bias

Concept Map for Health and Disease

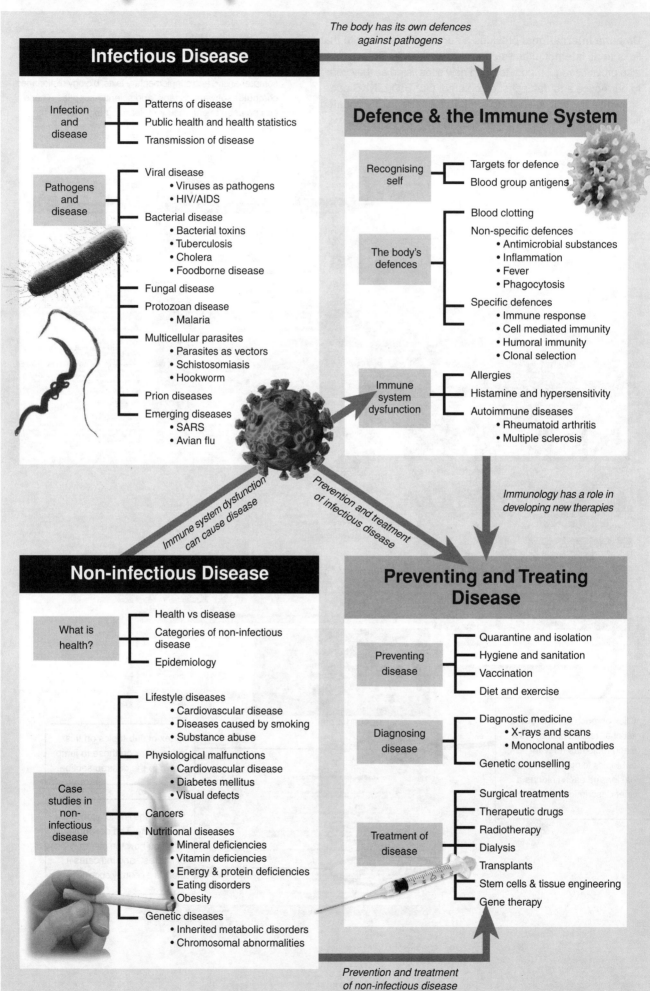

The body has its own defences against pathogens

Infectious Disease

Infection and disease
- Patterns of disease
- Public health and health statistics
- Transmission of disease

Pathogens and disease
- Viral disease
  - Viruses as pathogens
  - HIV/AIDS
- Bacterial disease
  - Bacterial toxins
  - Tuberculosis
  - Cholera
  - Foodborne disease
- Fungal disease
- Protozoan disease
  - Malaria
- Multicellular parasites
  - Parasites as vectors
  - Schistosomiasis
  - Hookworm
- Prion diseases
- Emerging diseases
  - SARS
  - Avian flu

Defence & the Immune System

Recognising self
- Targets for defence
- Blood group antigens

The body's defences
- Blood clotting
- Non-specific defences
  - Antimicrobial substances
  - Inflammation
  - Fever
  - Phagocytosis
- Specific defences
  - Immune response
  - Cell mediated immunity
  - Humoral immunity
  - Clonal selection

Immune system dysfunction
- Allergies
- Histamine and hypersensitivity
- Autoimmune diseases
  - Rheumatoid arthritis
  - Multiple sclerosis

Immune system dysfunction can cause disease

Prevention and treatment of infectious disease

Immunology has a role in developing new therapies

Non-infectious Disease

What is health?
- Health vs disease
- Categories of non-infectious disease
- Epidemiology

Case studies in non-infectious disease
- Lifestyle diseases
  - Cardiovascular disease
  - Diseases caused by smoking
  - Substance abuse
- Physiological malfunctions
  - Cardiovascular disease
  - Diabetes mellitus
  - Visual defects
- Cancers
- Nutritional diseases
  - Mineral deficiencies
  - Vitamin deficiencies
  - Energy & protein deficiencies
  - Eating disorders
  - Obesity
- Genetic diseases
  - Inherited metabolic disorders
  - Chromosomal abnormalities

Preventing and Treating Disease

Preventing disease
- Quarantine and isolation
- Hygiene and sanitation
- Vaccination
- Diet and exercise

Diagnosing disease
- Diagnostic medicine
  - X-rays and scans
  - Monoclonal antibodies
- Genetic counselling

Treatment of disease
- Surgical treatments
- Therapeutic drugs
- Radiotherapy
- Dialysis
- Transplants
- Stem cells & tissue engineering
- Gene therapy

Prevention and treatment of non-infectious disease

Resources Information

Your set textbook should always be a starting point for information, but there are also many other resources available. A list of readily available resources is provided below. Access to the publishers of these resources can be made directly from Biozone's web site through our resources hub: **www.thebiozone.com/resource-hub.html**. Please note that our listing of any product in this workbook does not denote Biozone's endorsement of it.

Supplementary Texts

Chenn, P., 1997.
Microorganisms and Biotechnology, 176 pp.
ISBN: 0-71957-509-5
Good coverage of the nature of microorganisms, their culture and growth, and their roles in biotechnology. It includes chapters on the genetic engineering of microbes and enzyme technology.

Clegg, C.J., 2002.
Microbes in Action, 92 pp.
ISBN: 0-71957-554-0
Microbes and their roles in disease and biotechnology. It includes material on the diversity of the microbial world, microbiological techniques, and a short account of enzyme technology.

Freeland, P., 1999
Hodder Advanced Science: Microbes, Medicine, and Commerce, 160 pp.
Publisher: Hodder and Stoughton
ISBN: 0340731036
Comments: *Coverage of biotechnology, microbiology, pathology, and immunity.*

Fullick, A., 1998
Human Health and Disease, 162 pp.
Publisher: Heinemann Educational Publishers
ISBN: 0435570919
Comments: *An excellent supplement for courses with modules in human health and disease. Includes infectious and non-infectious disease.*

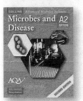

Hudson, T. and K. Mannion, 2001.
Microbes and Disease, 104 pp.
ISBN: 0-00-327742-9
Coverage of selected aspects of microbiology including the culture and applications of bacteria, and the role of bacteria and viruses in disease. Immunity, vaccination, and antimicrobial drug use are covered in the concluding chapter.

Murray, P. & N. Owens, 2001.
Behaviour and Populations, 82 pp.
ISBN: 0-00-327743-7
This text covers an eclectic range of topics including patterns of behaviour, reproduction and its control, human growth and development, human populations, aspects of infectious disease, and issues related to health and lifestyle.

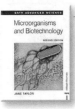

Taylor, J., 2001.
Microorganisms and Biotechnology, 192 pp.
Publisher: NelsonThornes. Available in Australia through Thomson Learning
ISBN: 0-17-448255-8
Comments: *Good coverage of this topic, including pathogens and disease, defence, and the use of microbes in industry and medicine.*

Biology Dictionaries

Access to a good biology dictionary is useful when dealing with biological terms. Some of the titles available are listed below. Link to the relevant publisher via Biozone's resources hub or by typing: **www.thebiozone.com/resources/dictionaries-pg1.html**

Clamp, A. **AS/A-Level Biology. Essential Word Dictionary**, 2000, 161 pp. Philip Allan Updates. **ISBN**: 0-86003-372-4.
Carefully selected essential words for AS and A2. Concise definitions are supported by further explanation and illustrations where required.

Hale, W.G., J.P. Margham, & V.A. Saunders. **Collins: Dictionary of Biology** 3 ed. 2003, 672 pp. HarperCollins. **ISBN**: 0-00-714709-0.
Updated to take in the latest developments in biology from the Human Genome Project to advancements in cloning (new edition pending).

Henderson, I.F, W.D. Henderson, and E. Lawrence. **Henderson's Dictionary of Biological Terms**, 1999, 736 pp. Prentice Hall. **ISBN**: 0582414989
This edition has been updated, rewritten for clarity, and reorganised for ease of use. An essential reference and the dictionary of choice for many.

McGraw-Hill (ed). **McGraw-Hill Dictionary of Bioscience**, 2 ed., 2002, 662 pp. McGraw-Hill. **ISBN**: 0-07-141043-0
22 000 entries encompassing more than 20 areas of the life sciences. It includes synonyms, acronyms, abbreviations, and pronunciations for all terms.

Periodicals, Magazines, & Journals

Biological Sciences Review: *An informative quarterly publication for biology students.* Enquiries: Philip Allan Publishers, Market Place, Deddington, Oxfordshire OX 15 OSE **Tel**: 01869 338652 **Fax**: 01869 338803 **E-mail**: sales@philipallan.co.uk *or subscribe from their web site.*

New Scientist: *Widely available weekly magazine with research summaries and features.* Enquiries: Reed Business Information Ltd, 51 Wardour St. London WIV 4BN **Tel**: (UK and intl):+44 (0) 1444 475636 **E-mail**: ns.subs@qss-uk.com *or subscribe from their web site.*

Scientific American: *A monthly magazine containing specialist features. Articles range in level of reading difficulty and assumed knowledge.* Subscription enquiries: 415 Madison Ave. New York. NY10017-1111 **Tel**: (outside North America): 515-247-7631 **Tel**: (US& Canada): 800-333-1199

School Science Review: *A quarterly journal which includes articles, reviews, and news on current research and curriculum development. Free to Ordinary Members of the ASE or available on subscription.* Enquiries: **Tel**: 01707 28300 **Email**: info@ase.org.uk *or visit their web site.*

The American Biology Teacher: *The peer-reviewed journal of the NABT. Published nine times a year and containing information and activities relevant to biology teachers.* Contact: NABT, 12030 Sunrise Valley Drive, #110, Reston, VA 20191-3409 **Web**: www.nabt.org

Defence and the Immune System

Defence mechanisms against disease: immune system function and dysfunction

Recognising self and non-self. Non-specific and specific defence mechanisms. Cell-mediated and humoral immunity. Autoimmunity.

Learning Objectives

☐ 1. Compile your own glossary from the **KEY WORDS** displayed in **bold type** in the learning objectives below.

Recognising Self and Non-self *(pages 10-11)*

☐ 2. Explain how a body is able to distinguish between self and non-self and comment on the importance of this.

☐ 3. Explain the nature of **major histocompatibility complex (MHC)** (including the HLA antigens) and its role in **self-recognition** and in determining tissue compatibility in transplant recipients.

☐ 4. Explain the basis of the **Rh** and **ABO blood group systems** in humans. Explain the consequences of blood type incompatibility in blood transfusions.

☐ 5. Discuss how **self-recognition** poses problems for tissue and organ transplants. Determine the physiological basis of transplant rejection and suggest how it may be avoided. Explain why it is so difficult to find compatible tissue and organ donors. Suggest how this problem might be solved in the future.

Defence Mechanisms

Non-specific defences *(pages 12-17)*

☐ 6. Explain what is meant by a **non-specific defence mechanism**. Distinguish between first and second lines of defence. Describe the nature and role of each of the following in protecting against pathogens:

Preventing pathogen entry (the first line of defence)
(a) Skin (including sweat and sebum production).
(b) Mucus-secreting and ciliated membranes.
(c) Body secretions (tears, urine, saliva, gastric juice).
(d) Blood clotting and the role of platelets.

Non-specific defence after pathogen entry (the second line of defence)
(e) Natural anti-bacterial and anti-viral proteins such as **interferon** and **complement.**
(f) The **inflammatory response, fever**, and cell death.
(g) **Phagocytosis** by phagocytes. Recognise the term phagocyte as referring to any of a number of phagocytic leucocytes (e.g. macrophages).

Specific defences *(pages 18, 23)*

☐ 7. Identify the **third line of defence** (specific resistance). Contrast specific and non-specific defences in terms of time for activation and **specificity** towards a pathogen.

☐ 8. Briefly explain what is meant by an **immune response**. Appreciate how the immune response involves recognition of, and response to, foreign material.

☐ 9. Explain the importance of retaining the memory of a foreign body and being able to respond to it in the future. Describe what is meant by the immune system having both **specificity** and **memory**. Providing examples, distinguish between **naturally acquired** and **artificially acquired immunity** and between **active** and **passive immunity**. Compare the duration of the immunity gained by active and passive means. Define: vaccine and immunisation.

☐ 10. Recognise the role of the **lymphatic system** in the production and transport of leucocytes.

The Immune System *(pages 18-22, 95-101)*

☐ 11. Distinguish between: **cell-mediated immunity** and **humoral (antibody-mediated immunity**

☐ 12. Explain the role of **lymphocytes** in the immune response. With respect to structure and function, distinguish between the two kinds of lymphocyte: **B cells** and **T cells**, and explain the origin of each type.

☐ 13. Recall that other types of white blood cells are involved in non-specific defence mechanisms.

☐ 14. Recognise the contribution to immunology of **Sir Frank McFarlane Burnet** through the development of the **clonal selection theory** (see #15-16 below).

☐ 15. Outline the theory of **clonal selection** and the basis of **immunological memory**. Explain how the immune system is able to respond to the large, unpredictable range of potential antigens in the environment.

☐ 16. Appreciate that self-tolerance occurs during development as a result of the selective destruction of the B cells that react to self-antigens.

☐ 17. Explain the role of the **thymus** in the immune response. Describe the nature, origin, and role of **macrophages** (a type of phagocyte). Appreciate the role of macrophages in processing and presenting foreign antigens and in stimulating lymphocyte activity.

Cell-mediated immunity

☐ 18. Describe the various roles of T lymphocytes in **cell-mediated immunity**. Describe how T cells recognise specific foreign antigens.

☐ 19. If required, describe the functional roles of the different named T cells, including the **cytotoxic (killer) T cells** (T_C) and the **helper T cells** (T_H). Identify the organisms/cells against which these T cells act.

☐ 20. Appreciate the role of T lymphocytes in the rejection of transplanted tissues and organs.

Humoral immunity

☐ 21. Define the terms: **antibody**, **antigen**, **immunoglobulin**. Name some common antigens and explain their role in provoking a specific immune response.

☐ 22. Describe the structure of an antibody identifying the constant and variable regions, and the **antigen binding site**. Relate antibody structure to function.

☐ 23. Explain antibody production, including how B cells bring about **humoral** (antibody-mediated) **immunity** to specific antigens. If required, provide an explanation of how antigens are presented, the role of **helper T cells**, and the activation and differentiation of B-cells.

☐ 24. Describe and contrast the functional roles of **plasma cells** and **memory cells** and recall the basis for immunological memory. Appreciate the role of immunological memory in long term immunity (ability to respond quickly to previously encountered antigens).

☐ 25. Describe the methods by which antibodies inactivate antigens and facilitate their destruction.

☐ 26. Describe what is meant by a **primary** and a **secondary response** to infection. Explain the role of these responses, as well as immune system memory, in the success of **vaccines** against specific pathogens (cross reference with the objectives and activities in the topic *Preventing and Treating Disease*).

☐ 27. Explain the principles behind the production of **monoclonal antibodies**. Describe their role in diagnosiing and treating disease (cross reference with the topic *Preventing and Treating Disease*).

Hypersensitivity Reactions *(pages 24-25)*

☐ 28. Explain what is meant by an **autoimmune disease** and provide examples. Recognise an allergic response as an inappropriate immune response to an **allergen**. Identify some of the common triggers for allergies in susceptible people.

☐ 29. With reference to **asthma** or **hayfever**, outline the role of the immune system in allergic reactions, including the role of **histamine** in these allergies.

See page 7 for additional details of this text:

■ Chenn, P. 1997. **Microorganisms and Biotechnology** (John Murray), chpt. 9 as required.

■ Freeland, P., 1999. **Microbes, Medicine and Commerce** (Hodder & Stoughton), chpt 6.

■ Fullick, A., 1998. **Human Health and Disease** (Heinemann), chpt. 2-3.

■ Hudson, T. & K. Mannion, 2001. **Microbes and Disease** (Collins), chpt. 6.

■ Taylor, J., 2001. **Microorganisms and Biotechnology** (NelsonThornes), chpt. 7.

See page 7 for details of publishers of periodicals:

STUDENT'S REFERENCE

Self-recognition & the immune system

■ **Skin, Scabs and Scars** Biol. Sci. Rev., 17(3) Feb. 2005, pp. 2-6. *The many roles of skin, including its importance in wound healing and the processes involved in its repair when damaged.*

■ **Inflammation** Biol. Sci. Rev., 17(1) Sept. 2004, pp. 18-20. *The role of this nonspecific defense response to tissue injury and infection. The processes involved in inflammation are discussed.*

■ **The Skin** Australasian Science 17(4), Summer 1996, pp. 9-12. *The skin as the body's largest organ has an important role in providing a physical and active barrier to the invasion of pathogens.*

■ **Antibodies** Biol. Sci. Rev., 11(3) January 1999, pp. 34-35. *The operation of the immune system and the production of antibodies (including procedures for producing monoclonal antibodies).*

■ **Lymphocytes - The Heart of the Immune System** Biol. Sci. Rev., 12 (1) September 1999 pp. 32-35. *An excellent account of the role of lymphocytes in the immune response (includes the types and actions of different lymphocytes).*

■ **Red Blood Cells** Biol. Sci. Rev., 11(2) November 1998, pp. 2-4. *The function of red blood cells, including their role in antigenic recognition.*

■ **Beware! Allergens** New Scientist, 22 January 2000 (Inside Science). *The allergic response: sensitisation and the role of the immune system.*

■ **Blood Group Antigens** Biol. Sci. Rev., 9(5) May 1997, pp. 10-13. *An excellent short account of the ABO and rhesus system in humans.*

■ **Fanning the Flames** New Scientist, 22 May 2004, pp. 40-43. *Inflammation is one of the first lines of internal defence, but it has been implicated in a host of disparate diseases.*

TEACHER'S REFERENCE

Self-recognition & the immune system

■ **Inside Trading** New Scientist, 26 June 1999, pp. 42-46. *How do we maintain a stable relationship with our microflora and protect ourselves from attack by pathogens?*

■ **Life, Death, and the Immune System** Scientific American, Sept. 1993. *An entire special issue on human infection, immune system, and disease.*

■ **Let Them Eat Dirt** New Scientist, 18 July 1998, pp. 26-31. *Effective, normal immune system function may require a certain level of early exposure to bacteria and other microorganisms..*

■ **The Long Arm of the Immune System** Sci. American, Nov. 2002, pp. 34-41. *The role of dendritic cells, a class of leucocytes with a role in activating the immune system (good extension).*

■ **How Interferons Fight Disease** Scientific American, May 1994, pp. 40-47. *The interferons of the human immune system and their active role in immune system function. Interferons can even activate immune system cells to attack tumors.*

■ **Immunotherapy** Biol. Sci. Rev., 15(1), Sept. 2002, pp. 39-41. *Medical research is uncovering ways in which our immune system can be used in developing vaccines for cancer.*

Hypersensitivity and immune failure

■ **Taming Lupus** Scientific American, March 2005, pp. 58-65. *An account of the autoimmune disorder, lupus: its causes, pathways to disease, triggers for disease onset, and possible treatments.*

■ **Filthy Friends** New Scientist,16 April 2005, pp. 34-39. *Early contact with a range of harmless microbes may be important in reducing the risk of hypersensitivity reactions.*

See pages 4-5 for details of how to access **Bio Links** from our web site: **www.thebiozone.com** From Bio Links, access sites under the topics:

GENERAL BIOLOGY ONLINE RESOURCES > Online Textbooks and Lecture Notes: • S-Cool! A level biology revision guide • Kimball's biology pages Learn.co.uk • Mr Biology's biology web site • Welcome to the biology web... *and others* > **General online biology resources:** • AP interactive animation • Acccess excellence • How stuff works • Ken's bioweb resources • National Association of Biology Teachers • Virtual library: Biosciences > **Glossaries:** • Animal anatomy glossary • Kimball's biology glossary

ANIMAL BIOLOGY: • Anatomy and physiology • Human physiology lecture notes ... *and others*

HEALTH & DISEASE > Defence and the Immune System: • Blood group antigens • Inducible defences against pathogens • National Institute of Allergy and infectious Disease • Microbiology and immunology • Primary immunodeficiency diseases • The immune system: An overview • Understanding the immune system • Tissue defences against pathogens • Welcome to the National Blood Service ... *and others*

Presentation MEDIA to support this topic:

Health & Disease CD-ROM: • Set 4: Defence & Immunity

Targets for Defence

In order for the body to present an effective defence against pathogens, it must first be able to recognise its own tissues (self). It must also ignore the normal microflora inhabiting our bodies and be able to deal with abnormal cells which periodically appear in the body and might develop into cancer. Failure of self/non-self recognition can lead to autoimmune disorders, in which the immune system mistakenly destroys its own tissues. The ability of the body to recognise its own molecules has implications for medical techniques such as tissue grafts, organ transplants, and blood transfusions. Incompatible tissues (correctly identified as foreign) are attacked by the body's immune system (rejection). Even a healthy pregnancy involves suppression of specific features of the self recognition system, allowing the mother to tolerate a nine month relationship with a foreign body (a foetus).

The Body's Natural Microbiota

After birth, normal and characteristic microbial populations begin to establish themselves on and in the body. A typical human body contains 1×10^{13} body cells, yet harbours 1×10^{14} bacterial cells. These microorganisms establish more or less permanent residence but, under normal conditions, do not cause disease. In fact, this normal microflora can benefit the host by preventing the overgrowth of harmful pathogens. They are not found throughout the entire body, but are located in certain regions.

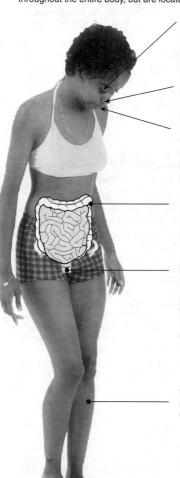

Eyes: The conjuctiva, a continuation of the skin or mucous membrane, contains a similar microbiota to the skin.

Nose and throat: Harbours a variety of microorganisms, e.g. *Staphylococcus spp.*

Mouth: Supports a large and diverse microbiota. It is an ideal microbial environment; high in moisture, warmth, and nutrient availability.

Large intestine: Contains the body's largest resident population of microbes because of its available moisture and nutrients.

Urinary and genital systems: The lower urethra in both sexes has a resident population; the vagina has a particular acid-tolerant population of microbes because of the low pH nature of its secretions.

Skin: Skin secretions prevent most of the microbes on the skin from becoming residents.

Distinguishing Self from Non-Self

The human immune system achieves self-recognition through the **major histocompatibility complex** (MHC). This is a cluster of tightly linked genes on chromosome 6 in humans. These genes code for protein molecules (MHC antigens) that are attached to the surface of body cells. They are used by the immune system to recognise its own or foreign material. **Class I MHC** antigens are located on the surface of virtually all human cells, but **Class II MHC** antigens are restricted to macrophages and the antibody-producing B-lymphocytes.

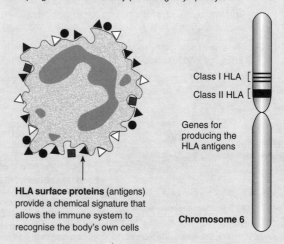

Class I HLA

Class II HLA

Genes for producing the HLA antigens

Chromosome 6

HLA surface proteins (antigens) provide a chemical signature that allows the immune system to recognise the body's own cells

Tissue Transplants

The MHC is responsible for the rejection of tissue grafts and organ transplants. Foreign MHC molecules are antigenic, causing the immune system to respond in the following way:

- T cells directly lyse the foreign cells

- Macrophages are activated by T cells and engulf foreign cells

- Antibodies are released that attack the foreign cell

- The complement system injures blood vessels supplying the graft or transplanted organ

To minimise this rejection, attempts are made to match the MHC of the organ donor to that of the recipient as closely as possible.

1. Explain why it is healthy to have a natural population of microbes on and inside the body: _____

_____

2. (a) Explain the nature and purpose of the major histocompatibility complex (MHC): _____

_____

_____

_____

(b) Explain the importance of such a self-recognition system: _____

_____

3. Name two situations when the body's recognition of 'self' is undesirable: _____

Blood Group Antigens

Blood groups classify blood according to the different marker proteins on the surface of red blood cells (RBCs). These marker proteins act as **antigens** and affect the ability of RBCs to provoke an immune response. The **ABO blood group** is the most important blood typing system in medical practice, because of the presence of anti-A and anti-B antibodies in nearly all people who lack the corresponding red cell antigens (these antibodies are carried in the plasma and are present at birth). If a patient is to receive blood from a blood donor, that blood must be compatible otherwise the red blood cells of the donated blood will clump together (agglutinate), break apart, and block capillaries. There is a small margin of safety in certain blood group combinations, because the volume of donated blood is usually relatively small and the donor's antibodies are quickly diluted in the plasma. In practice, blood is carefully matched, not only for ABO types, but for other types as well. Although human RBCs have more than 500 known antigens, fewer than 30 (in 9 blood groups) are regularly tested for when blood is donated for transfusion. The blood groups involved are: *ABO, Rh, MNS, P, Lewis, Lutheran, Kell, Duffy,* and *Kidd*. The ABO and rhesus (Rh) are the best known. Although blood typing has important applications in medicine, it can also be used to rule out individuals in cases of crime (or paternity) and establish a list of potential suspects (or fathers).

	Blood type A	**Blood type B**	**Blood type AB**	**Blood type O**
Antigens present on the **red blood cells**	antigen **A**	antigen **B**	antigens **A** and **B**	Neither antigen **A** nor **B**
Antibodies present in the **plasma**	Contains **anti-B** antibodies; but no antibodies that would attack its own antigen **A**	Contains **anti-A** antibodies; but no antibodies that would attack its own antigen **B**	Contains neither **anti-A** nor **anti-B** antibodies	Contains both **anti-A** and **anti-B** antibodies

Blood type	Frequency in UK Rh⁺	Frequency in UK Rh⁻	Antigen	Antibody	Can donate blood to:	Can receive blood from:
A	36%	7%	*A*	*anti-B*	*A, AB*	*A, O*
B	8%	1%				
AB	2%	1%				
O	38%	7%				

1. Complete the table above to show the antibodies and antigens in each blood group, and donor/recipient blood types:

2. In a hypothetical murder case, blood from both the victim and the murderer was left at the scene. There were five suspects under investigation:

   (a) Describe what blood typing could establish about the guilt or innocence of the suspects: _____

   _____

   (b) Identify what a blood typing could not establish: _____

   _____

   (c) Suggest how the murderer's identity could be firmly established (assuming that s/he was one of the five suspects):

   _____

   (d) Explain why blood typing is not used forensically to any great extent: _____

   _____

3. Explain why the discovery of the ABO system was such a significant medical breakthrough: _____

   _____

Blood Clotting and Defence

Apart from its transport role, **blood** has a role in the body's defence against infection and **haemostasis** (the prevention of bleeding and maintenance of blood volume). The tearing or puncturing of a blood vessel initiates **clotting**. Clotting is normally a rapid process that seals off the tear, preventing blood loss and the invasion of bacteria into the site. Clot formation is triggered by the release of clotting factors from the damaged cells at the site of the tear or puncture. A hardened clot forms a scab, which acts to prevent further blood loss and acts as a mechanical barrier to the entry of pathogens.

Blood Clotting

1 Injury to the lining of a blood vessels exposes collagen fibres to the blood. Platelets stick to the collagen fibres.

3 Platelets clump together. The platelet plug forms an emergency protection against blood loss.

When tissue is wounded, the blood quickly coagulates to prevent further blood loss and maintain the integrity of the circulatory system. For external wounds, clotting also prevents the entry of pathogens. Blood clotting involves a cascade of reactions involving at least twelve clotting factors in the blood. The end result is the formation of an insoluble network of fibres, which traps red blood cells and seals the wound.

Blood vessel

Endothelial cell

Red blood cell

Exposed collagen fibres

2 Platelet releases chemicals that make the surrounding platelets sticky

Platelet plug

4 A fibrin clot reinforces the seal. The clot traps blood cells and the clot eventually dries to form a **scab**.

Clotting factors from:

Platelets →

Damaged cells →

← Plasma clotting factors

← **Calcium**

Clotting factors catalyse the conversion of prothrombin (plasma protein) to thrombin (an active enzyme). Clotting factors include thromboplastin and factor VIII (antihaemophilia factor).

| Prothrombin | ⇒ | Thrombin |

Fibrin clot traps red blood cells

| Fibrinogen | ⇒ | Fibrin |

Hydrolysis

1. Explain two roles of the blood clotting system in internal defence and haemostasis:

   (a) _____

   (b) _____

2. Explain the role of each of the following in the sequence of events leading to a blood clot:

   (a) Injury: _____

   (b) Release of chemicals from platelets: _____

   _____

   (c) Clumping of platelets at the wound site: _____

   _____

   (d) Formation of a fibrin clot: _____

   _____

3. (a) Explain the role of clotting factors in the blood in formation of the clot: _____

   _____

   (b) Explain why these clotting factors are not normally present in the plasma: _____

   _____

4. (a) Name one inherited disease caused by the absence of a clotting factor: _____

   (b) Name the clotting factor involved: _____

The Body's Defences

If microorganisms never encountered resistance from our body defences, we would be constantly ill and would eventually die of various diseases. Fortunately, in most cases our defences prevent this from happening. Some of these defences are designed to keep microorganisms from entering the body. Other defences remove the microorganisms if they manage to get inside. Further defences attack the microorganisms if they remain inside the body. The ability to ward off disease through the various defence mechanisms is called **resistance**. The lack of resistance, or vulnerability to disease, is known as **susceptibility**. One form of

defence is referred to as **non-specific resistance**, and includes defences that protect us from any pathogen. This includes a first line of defence such as the physical barriers to infection (skin and mucous membranes) and a second line of defence (phagocytes, inflammation, fever, and antimicrobial substances). **Specific resistance** is a third line of defence that forms the **immune response** and targets specific pathogens. Specialised cells of the immune system, called lymphocytes, produce specific proteins called antibodies which are produced against specific antigens.

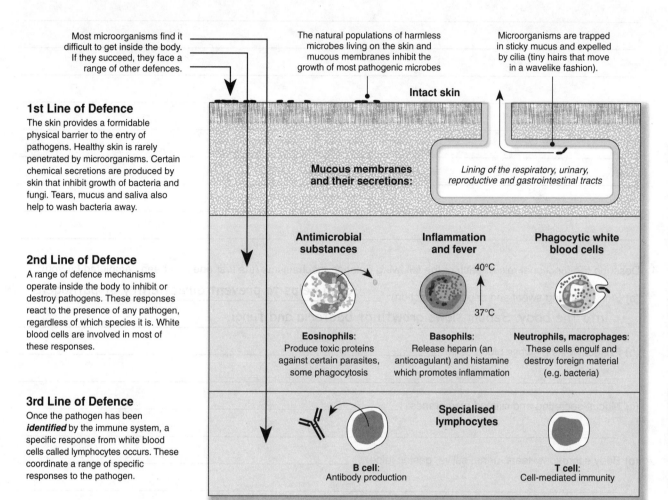

Most microorganisms find it difficult to get inside the body. If they succeed, they face a range of other defences.

The natural populations of harmless microbes living on the skin and mucous membranes inhibit the growth of most pathogenic microbes

Microorganisms are trapped in sticky mucus and expelled by cilia (tiny hairs that move in a wavelike fashion).

Intact skin

Mucous membranes and their secretions:

Lining of the respiratory, urinary, reproductive and gastrointestinal tracts

1st Line of Defence

The skin provides a formidable physical barrier to the entry of pathogens. Healthy skin is rarely penetrated by microorganisms. Certain chemical secretions are produced by skin that inhibit growth of bacteria and fungi. Tears, mucus and saliva also help to wash bacteria away.

2nd Line of Defence

A range of defence mechanisms operate inside the body to inhibit or destroy pathogens. These responses react to the presence of any pathogen, regardless of which species it is. White blood cells are involved in most of these responses.

3rd Line of Defence

Once the pathogen has been *identified* by the immune system, a specific response from white blood cells called lymphocytes occurs. These coordinate a range of specific responses to the pathogen.

Antimicrobial substances

Eosinophils: Produce toxic proteins against certain parasites, some phagocytosis

Inflammation and fever

40°C
37°C

Basophils: Release heparin (an anticoagulant) and histamine which promotes inflammation

Phagocytic white blood cells

Neutrophils, macrophages: These cells engulf and destroy foreign material (e.g. bacteria)

Specialised lymphocytes

B cell: Antibody production

T cell: Cell-mediated immunity

Defence & the Immune System

1. Compare and contrast the type of response against pathogens carried out by each of the three levels of defence:

_____

_____

_____

_____

_____

_____

_____

_____

_____

_____

_____

2. Distinguish between specific and non-specific resistance: _____

_____

_____

_____

3. Describe features of the different types of white blood cells and explain how these relate to their role in the second line of defence:

_____

_____

_____

_____

_____

_____

_____

_____

_____

_____

4. Describe the functional role of each of the following defence mechanisms (the first one has been completed for you):

(a) Skin (including sweat and sebum production): _Skin helps to prevent direct entry of pathogens into the body. Sebum slows growth of bacteria and fungi._

(b) Phagocytosis by white blood cells: _____

_____

(c) Mucus-secreting and ciliated membranes: _____

_____

(d) Body secretions: tears, urine, saliva, gastric juice: _____

_____

(e) Natural antimicrobial proteins (e.g. interferon): _____

_____

(f) Antibody production: _____

_____

(g) Fever: _____

_____

(h) Cell-mediated immunity: _____

_____

(i) The inflammatory response: _____

_____

5. Infection with HIV results in the progressive destruction of T lymphocytes. Suggest why this leads to an increasing number of opportunistic infections in AIDS sufferers:

_____

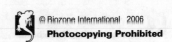

The Action of Phagocytes

Human cells that ingest microbes and digest them by the process of **phagocytosis** are called **phagocytes**. All are types of white blood cells. During many kinds of infections, especially bacterial infections, the total number of white blood cells increases by two to four times the normal number. The ratio of various white blood cell types changes during the course of an infection.

How a Phagocyte Destroys Microbes

1 Detection
Phagocyte detects microbes by the chemicals they give off (chemotaxis) and sticks the microbes to its surface.

2 Ingestion
The microbe is engulfed by the phagocyte wrapping pseudopodia around it to form a vesicle.

3 Phagosome forms
A phagosome (phagocytic vesicle) is formed, which encloses the microbes in a membrane.

4 Fusion with lysosome
Phagosome fuses with a lysosome (which contains powerful enzymes that can digest the microbe).

5 Digestion
The microbes are broken down by enzymes into their chemical constituents.

6 Discharge
Indigestible material is discharged from the phagocyte cell.

Phagocytes are amoeba-like cells that can extend parts of the cell in different directions. These extensions are called **pseudopodia** are used to engulf microbes.

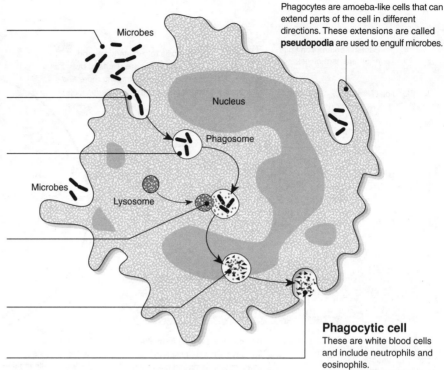

Microbes
Nucleus
Phagosome
Microbes
Lysosome

Phagocytic cell
These are white blood cells and include neutrophils and eosinophils.

The Interaction of Microbes and Phagocytes

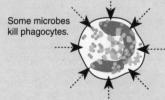

Some microbes kill phagocytes.

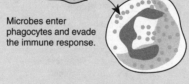

Microbes enter phagocytes and evade the immune response.

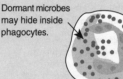

Dormant microbes may hide inside phagocytes.

Some microbes kill phagocytes
Some microbes produce toxins that can actually kill phagocytes, e.g. toxin-producing staphylococci and the dental plaque-forming bacteria *Actinobacillus*.

Microbes evade immune system
Some microbes can evade the immune system by entering phagocytes. The microbes prevent fusion of the lysosome with the phagosome and multiply inside the phagocyte, almost filling it. Examples include *Chlamydia*, *Mycobacterium tuberculosis*, *Shigella*, and malarial parasites.

Dormant microbes hide inside
Some microbes can remain dormant inside the phagocyte for months or years at a time. Examples include the microbes that cause brucellosis and tularemia.

1. Identify the white blood cells capable of phagocytosis: _____
_____

2. Describe how a blood sample from a patient may be used to determine whether they have a microbial infection (without looking for the microbes themselves):
_____
_____

3. Explain how some microbes are able to overcome phagocytic cells and use them to their advantage:
_____
_____

Inflammation

Damage to the body's tissues can be caused by physical agents (e.g. sharp objects, heat, radiant energy, or electricity), microbial infection, or chemical agents (e.g. gases, acids and bases). The damage triggers a defensive response called **inflammation**. It is usually characterised by four symptoms: pain, redness, heat and swelling. The inflammatory response is beneficial and has the following functions: (1) to destroy the cause of the infection and remove it and its products from the body; (2) if this fails, to limit the effects on the body by confining the infection to a small area; (3) replacing or repairing tissue damaged by the infection. The process of inflammation can be divided into three distinct stages. These are described below.

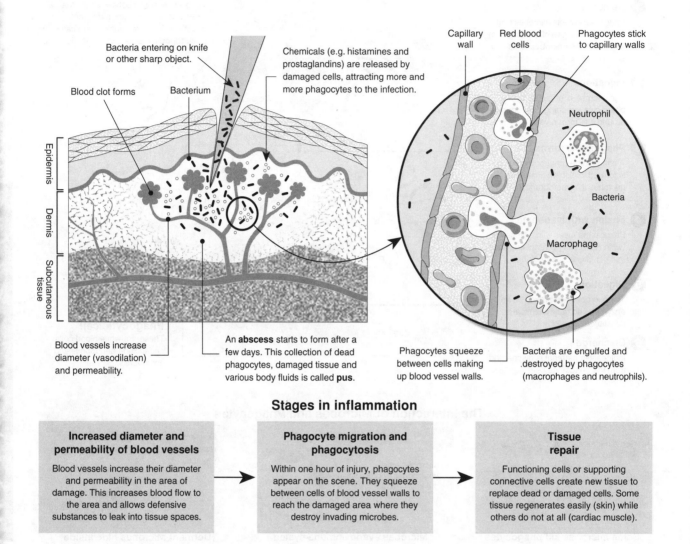

Stages in inflammation

Increased diameter and permeability of blood vessels	**Phagocyte migration and phagocytosis**	**Tissue repair**
Blood vessels increase their diameter and permeability in the area of damage. This increases blood flow to the area and allows defensive substances to leak into tissue spaces.	Within one hour of injury, phagocytes appear on the scene. They squeeze between cells of blood vessel walls to reach the damaged area where they destroy invading microbes.	Functioning cells or supporting connective cells create new tissue to replace dead or damaged cells. Some tissue regenerates easily (skin) while others do not at all (cardiac muscle).

1. Outline the three **stages** of inflammation and identify the beneficial role of each stage:

    (a) _____

    _____

    (b) _____

    _____

    (c) _____

    _____

2. Identify two features of phagocytes important in the response to microbial invasion: _____

    _____

3. State the role of histamines and prostaglandins in inflammation: _____

4. Explain why pus forms at the site of infection: _____

Fever

Fever is a medical symptom that describes an increase in internal body temperature to levels that are above normal (36.2 to 37.2°C). Up to a point, fever is beneficial, since it assists a number of the defence processes. The release of the protein **interleukin-1** aids in resetting the body's thermostat to a higher level and helps step up the production of **T cells** (lymphocytes). Fever also intensifies the effect of the anti-viral protein **interferon**

and is believed to inhibit the growth of some bacteria and viruses. It increases heart rate so that white blood cells are delivered to sites of infection more rapidly and may assist more rapid tissue repair by speeding up metabolic reactions. Fevers of less than 40°C do not need treatment for **hyperthermia**, but excessive fever requires prompt attention (particularly in children). Death usually results if body temperature rises to 44.4 to 45.5°C.

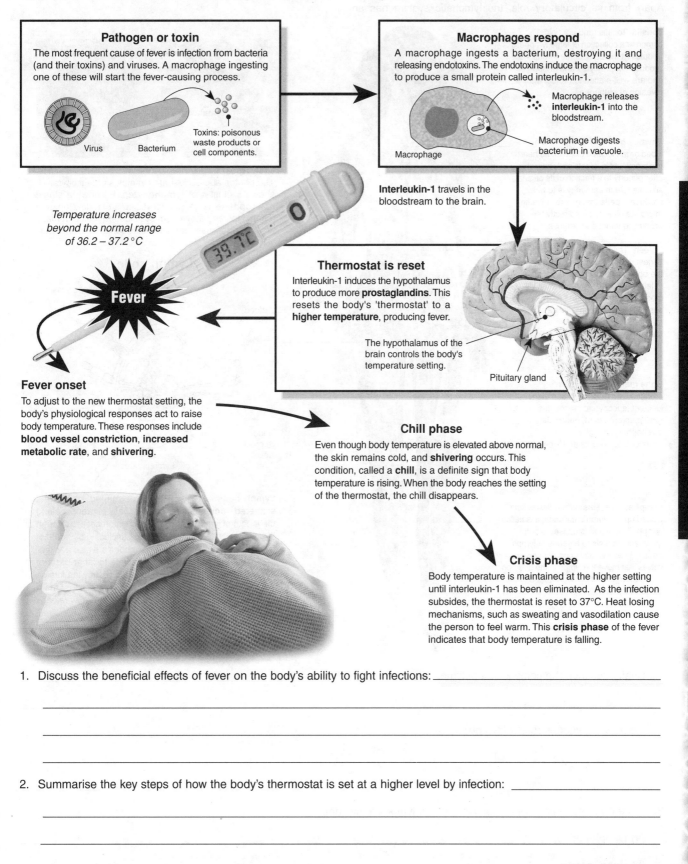

Pathogen or toxin

The most frequent cause of fever is infection from bacteria (and their toxins) and viruses. A macrophage ingesting one of these will start the fever-causing process.

Virus   Bacterium   Toxins: poisonous waste products or cell components.

Macrophages respond

A macrophage ingests a bacterium, destroying it and releasing endotoxins. The endotoxins induce the macrophage to produce a small protein called interleukin-1.

Macrophage releases **interleukin-1** into the bloodstream.

Macrophage digests bacterium in vacuole.

Macrophage

Interleukin-1 travels in the bloodstream to the brain.

Temperature increases beyond the normal range of 36.2 – 37.2 °C

Fever

Thermostat is reset

Interleukin-1 induces the hypothalamus to produce more **prostaglandins**. This resets the body's 'thermostat' to a **higher temperature**, producing fever.

The hypothalamus of the brain controls the body's temperature setting.

Pituitary gland

Fever onset

To adjust to the new thermostat setting, the body's physiological responses act to raise body temperature. These responses include **blood vessel constriction**, **increased metabolic rate**, and **shivering**.

Chill phase

Even though body temperature is elevated above normal, the skin remains cold, and **shivering** occurs. This condition, called a **chill**, is a definite sign that body temperature is rising. When the body reaches the setting of the thermostat, the chill disappears.

Crisis phase

Body temperature is maintained at the higher setting until interleukin-1 has been eliminated. As the infection subsides, the thermostat is reset to 37°C. Heat losing mechanisms, such as sweating and vasodilation cause the person to feel warm. This **crisis phase** of the fever indicates that body temperature is falling.

1. Discuss the beneficial effects of fever on the body's ability to fight infections: _____

_____

_____

_____

2. Summarise the key steps of how the body's thermostat is set at a higher level by infection: _____

_____

_____

_____

The Lymphatic System

Fluid leaks out from capillaries and forms the tissue fluid, which is similar in composition to plasma but lacks large proteins. This fluid bathes the tissues, supplying them with nutrients and oxygen, and removing wastes. Some of the tissue fluid returns directly into the capillaries, but some drains back into the blood circulation through a network of lymph vessels. This fluid, called **lymph**, is similar to tissue fluid, but contains more leucocytes. Apart from its circulatory role, the lymphatic system has an important function in the immune response. Lymph nodes are the primary sites where the destruction of pathogens and other foreign substances occurs. A lymph node that is fighting an infection becomes swollen and hard as the lymph cells reproduce rapidly to increase their numbers. The thymus, spleen, and bone marrow also contribute leucocytes to the lymphatic and circulatory systems.

Tonsils Tonsils (and adenoids) comprise a collection of large lymphatic nodules at the back of the throat. They produce lymphocytes and antibodies and are well-placed to protect against invasion of pathogens

Thymus gland: The thymus is a two-obed organ located close to he heart It is prominent in infants and diminishes after puberty to a fraction of its original size. Its role in immunity is to help produce **T cells** that destroy invading microbes directly or indirectly by producing various substances.

Spleen The oval spleen is the largest mass of lymphatic tissue in the body, measuring about 12 cm in length. It stores and releases blood in case of demand (e.g. in cases of bleeding), produces mature **B cells**, and destroys bacteria by phagocytosis.

Bone marrow: Bone marrow produces red blood cells and many kinds of leucocytes: monocytes (and macrophages), neutrophils, eosinophils, basophils, and lymphocytes (B cells and T cells).

Lymphatic vessels When tissue fluid is picked up by lymph capillaries, it is called ymph The lymph is passed along lymphatic vessels to a series of lymph nodes. These vessels contain one-way valves that move the lymph in the direction of the heart until it is reintroduced to the blood at the subclavian veins

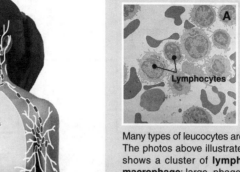

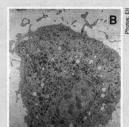

Many types of leucocytes are involved in internal defence. The photos above illustrate examples of leucocytes. **A** shows a cluster of **lymphocytes**. **B** shows a single **macrophage**: large, phagocytic cells that develop from monocytes and move from the blood to reside in many organs and tissues, including the spleen and lymph nodes.

Lymph node

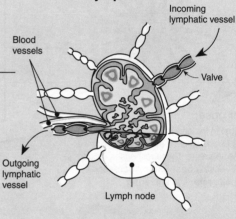

Lymph nodes are oval or bean-shaped structures, scattered throughout the body, usually in groups, along the length of lymphatic vessels. As lymph passes through the nodes, it filters foreign particles (including pathogens) by trapping them in fibres. Lymph nodes are also a "store" of **lymphocytes**, which may circulate to other parts of the body. Once trapped, macrophages destroy the foreign substances by phagocytosis. T cells may destroy them by releasing various products, and/or B cells may release antibodies that destroy them.

1. Briefly describe the composition of lymph: _____

_____

2. Discuss the various roles of lymph: _____

_____

_____

3. State one role of each of the following in the lymphatic system:

(a) Lymph nodes: _____

(b) Bone marrow: _____

The Immune System

The efficient internal defence provided by the immune system is based on its ability to respond specifically against a foreign substance and its ability to hold a memory of this response. There are two main components of the immune system: the humoral and the cell-mediated responses. They work separately and together to protect us from disease. The **humoral immune response** is associated with the serum (non-cellular part of the blood) and involves the action of **antibodies** secreted by B cell lymphocytes. Antibodies are found in extracellular fluids including lymph, plasma, and mucus secretions. The humoral response protects the body against circulating viruses, and bacteria and their toxins. The **cell-mediated immune response** is associated with the production of specialised lymphocytes called **T cells**. It is most effective against bacteria and viruses located within host cells, as well as against parasitic protozoa, fungi, and worms. This system is also an important defence against cancer, and is responsible for the rejection of transplanted tissue. Both B and T cells develop from stem cells located in the liver of foetuses and the bone marrow of adults. T cells complete their development in the thymus, whilst the B cells mature in the bone marrow.

Lymphocytes and their Functions

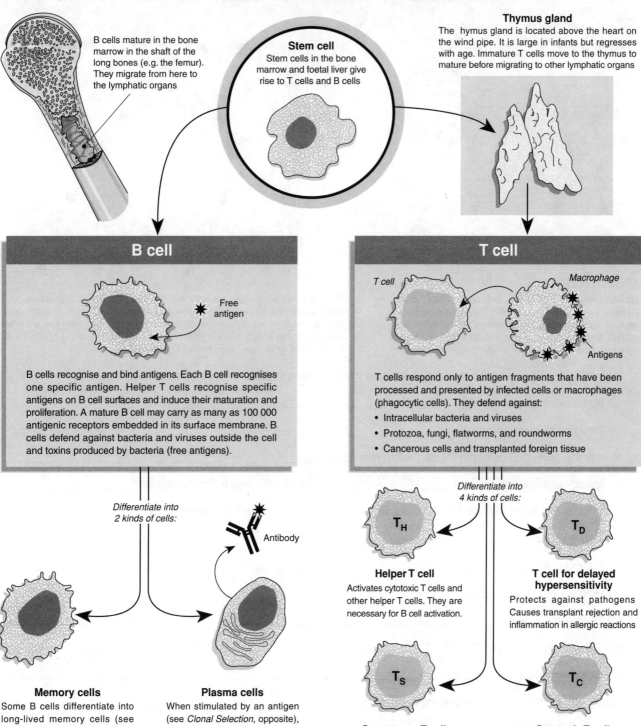

B cells mature in the bone marrow in the shaft of the long bones (e.g. the femur). They migrate from here to the lymphatic organs

Stem cell
Stem cells in the bone marrow and foetal liver give rise to T cells and B cells

Thymus gland
The hymus gland is located above the heart on the wind pipe. It is large in infants but regresses with age. Immature T cells move to the thymus to mature before migrating to other lymphatic organs

B cell

Free antigen

B cells recognise and bind antigens. Each B cell recognises one specific antigen. Helper T cells recognise specific antigens on B cell surfaces and induce their maturation and proliferation. A mature B cell may carry as many as 100 000 antigenic receptors embedded in its surface membrane. B cells defend against bacteria and viruses outside the cell and toxins produced by bacteria (free antigens).

T cell

T cell   Macrophage

Antigens

T cells respond only to antigen fragments that have been processed and presented by infected cells or macrophages (phagocytic cells). They defend against:
- Intracellular bacteria and viruses
- Protozoa, fungi, flatworms, and roundworms
- Cancerous cells and transplanted foreign tissue

Differentiate into 2 kinds of cells:

Antibody

Differentiate into 4 kinds of cells:

T_H

T_D

Helper T cell
Activates cytotoxic T cells and other helper T cells. They are necessary for B cell activation.

T cell for delayed hypersensitivity
Protects against pathogens Causes transplant rejection and inflammation in allergic reactions

T_S

T_C

Memory cells
Some B cells differentiate into long-lived memory cells (see opposite). When these cells encounter the same antigen again (even years or decades later), they rapidly differentiate into antibody-producing plasma cells

Plasma cells
When stimulated by an antigen (see *Clonal Selection*, opposite), some B cells differentiate into plasma cells, which secrete antibodies into the blood system. The antibodies then inactivate the circulating antigens

Suppressor T cell
Regulates immune response by turning it off when no more antigen is present.

Cytotoxic T cell
Destroys target cells on contact. Recognises tumour (cancer) or virus infected cells by their surface (antigens and MHC markers).

Defence & the Immune System

Code: A 2

The immune system has the ability to respond to the large and unpredictable range of potential antigens encountered in the environment. The diagram below explains how this ability is based on **clonal selection** after antigen exposure. The example illustrated is for B cell lymphocytes. In the same way, a T cell stimulated by a specific antigen will multiply and develop into different types of T cells. Clonal selection and differentiation of lymphocytes provide the basis for **immunological memory**.

Five (a-e) of the many, randomly generated B cells. Each one can recognise only one specific antigen.

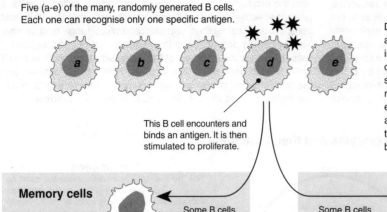

This B cell encounters and binds an antigen. It is then stimulated to proliferate.

Clonal Selection Theory

During development, millions of randomly generated B cells are formed. These are able to recognise many different antigens, including those never before encountered. Each B cell has one specific type of antigenic receptor on its surface whose shape is identical to the antibodies that the cell can make. The receptor will react only to a single antigen. When a B cell encounters its specific antigen, it responds by proliferating into a large clone of cells, all with the same genetic material and the same kind of antibody. This is called **clonal selection** because the antigen selects the B cells that will proliferate.

Memory cells

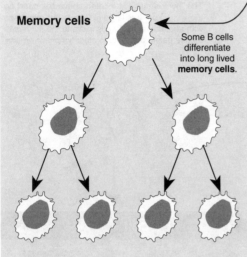

Plasma cells

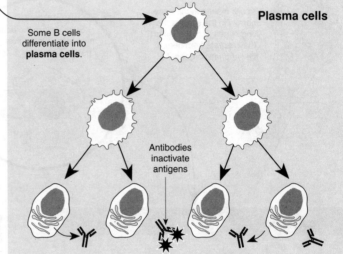

Antibodies inactivate antigens

Some B cells differentiate into long lived **memory cells**. These are retained in the lymph nodes to provide future immunity (**immunological memory**). In the event of a second infection, B-memory cells react more quickly and vigorously than the initial B-cell reaction to the first infection.

Plasma cells secrete antibodies specific to the antigen that stimulated their development. Each plasma cell lives for only a few days, but can produce about 2000 antibody molecules per second. Note that during development, any B cells that react to the body's own antigens are selectively destroyed in a process that leads to **self tolerance** (acceptance of the body's own tissues).

1. State the general action of the two major divisions in the immune system:

   (a) Humoral immune system: _____

   (b) Cell-mediated immune system: _____

2. Identify the origin of B cells and T cells (before maturing): _____

3. (a) Identify where B cells mature: _____ (b) Identify where T cells mature: _____

4. State briefly the function of each of the following cells in the immune system response:

   (a) Memory cells: _____

   (b) Plasma cells: _____

   (c) Helper T cells: _____

   (d) Suppressor T cells: _____

   (e) Delayed hypersensitivity T cells: _____

   (f) Cytotoxic T cells: _____

5. Briefly explain the basis of **immunological memory**: _____

_____

_____

Antibodies

Antibodies and antigens play key roles in the response of the immune system. Antigens are foreign molecules that are able to bind to antibodies (or T cell receptors) and provoke a specific immune response. Antigens include potentially damaging microbes and their toxins (see below) as well as substances such as pollen grains, blood cell surface molecules, and the surface proteins on transplanted tissues. **Antibodies** (also called immunoglobulins) are proteins that are made in response to antigens. They are secreted into the plasma where they circulate and can recognise, bind to, and help to destroy antigens. There are 5 classes of **immunoglobulins**. Each plays a different role in the immune response (including destroying protozoan parasites, enhancing phagocytosis, protecting mucous surfaces, and neutralising toxins and viruses). The human body can produce an estimated 100 million antibodies, recognising many different antigens, including those it has never encountered. Each type of antibody is highly specific to only one particular antigen. The ability of the immune system to recognise and ignore the antigenic properties of its own tissues occurs early in development and is called **self-tolerance**. Exceptions occur when the immune system malfunctions and the body attacks its own tissues, causing an **autoimmune disorder**.

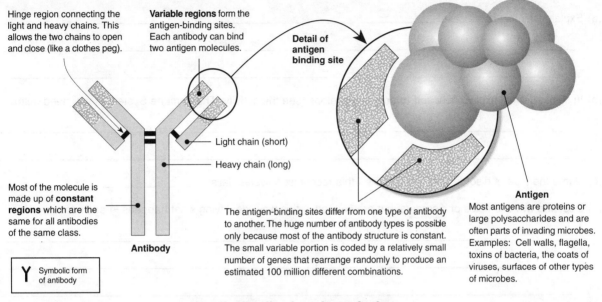

Hinge region connecting the light and heavy chains. This allows the two chains to open and close (like a clothes peg).

Variable regions form the antigen-binding sites. Each antibody can bind two antigen molecules.

Detail of antigen binding site

Light chain (short)

Heavy chain (long)

Most of the molecule is made up of **constant regions** which are the same for all antibodies of the same class.

Antibody

Y Symbolic form of antibody

The antigen-binding sites differ from one type of antibody to another. The huge number of antibody types is possible only because most of the antibody structure is constant. The small variable portion is coded by a relatively small number of genes that rearrange randomly to produce an estimated 100 million different combinations.

Antigen
Most antigens are proteins or large polysaccharides and are often parts of invading microbes. Examples: Cell walls, flagella, toxins of bacteria, the coats of viruses, surfaces of other types of microbes.

How Antibodies Inactivate Antigens

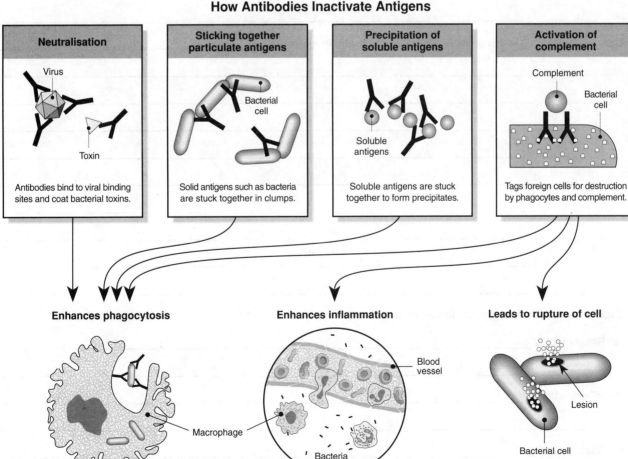

Neutralisation

Virus

Toxin

Antibodies bind to viral binding sites and coat bacterial toxins.

Sticking together particulate antigens

Bacterial cell

Solid antigens such as bacteria are stuck together in clumps.

Precipitation of soluble antigens

Soluble antigens

Soluble antigens are stuck together to form precipitates.

Activation of complement

Complement

Bacterial cell

Tags foreign cells for destruction by phagocytes and complement.

Enhances phagocytosis

Macrophage

Enhances inflammation

Blood vessel

Bacteria

Leads to rupture of cell

Lesion

Bacterial cell

Defence & the Immune System

Code: RA 2

1. Distinguish between an antibody and an antigen: _____

_____

_____

_____

_____

_____

2. It is necessary for the immune system to clearly distinguish cells and proteins made by the body, from foreign ones.

   (a) Explain why this is the case: _____

_____

_____

   (b) In simple terms, explain how **self tolerance** develops (see the activity "The Immune System" if you need help):

_____

_____

   (c) Name the type of disorder that results when this recognition system fails: _____

   (d) Describe two examples of disorders that are caused in this way, identifying what happens in each case:

_____

_____

_____

_____

3. Discuss the ways in which antibodies work to inactivate antigens: _____

_____

_____

_____

_____

_____

_____

_____

_____

_____

4. Explain how antibody activity enhances or leads to:

   (a) Phagocytosis: _____

_____

   (b) Inflammation: _____

_____

   (c) Bacterial cell lysis: _____

_____

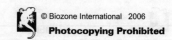

Acquired Immunity

We have natural or **innate resistance** to certain illnesses; examples include most diseases of other animal species. **Acquired immunity** refers to the protection an animal develops against certain types of microbes or foreign substances. Immunity can be acquired either passively or actively and is developed during an individual's lifetime. **Active immunity** develops when a person is exposed to microorganisms or foreign substances and the immune system responds. **Passive immunity** is acquired when antibodies are transferred from one person to another. Recipients do not make the antibodies themselves and the effect lasts only as long as the antibodies are present, usually several weeks or months. Immunity may also be **naturally acquired**, through natural exposure to microbes, or **artificially acquired** as a result of medical treatment.

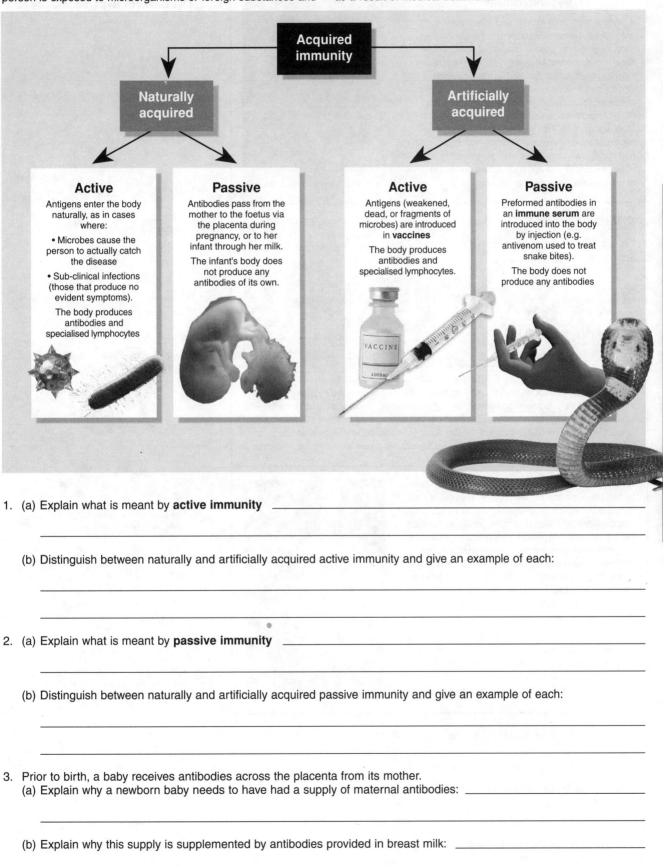

Acquired immunity

Naturally acquired

Artificially acquired

Active

Antigens enter the body naturally, as in cases where:

• Microbes cause the person to actually catch the disease

• Sub-clinical infections (those that produce no evident symptoms).

The body produces antibodies and specialised lymphocytes

Passive

Antibodies pass from the mother to the foetus via the placenta during pregnancy, or to her infant through her milk.

The infant's body does not produce any antibodies of its own.

Active

Antigens (weakened, dead, or fragments of microbes) are introduced in **vaccines**

The body produces antibodies and specialised lymphocytes.

Passive

Preformed antibodies in an **immune serum** are introduced into the body by injection (e.g. antivenom used to treat snake bites).

The body does not produce any antibodies

VACCINE
2000ml

Defence & the Immune System

1. (a) Explain what is meant by **active immunity** _____

_____

(b) Distinguish between naturally and artificially acquired active immunity and give an example of each:

_____

_____

2. (a) Explain what is meant by **passive immunity** _____

_____

(b) Distinguish between naturally and artificially acquired passive immunity and give an example of each:

_____

_____

3. Prior to birth, a baby receives antibodies across the placenta from its mother.
(a) Explain why a newborn baby needs to have had a supply of maternal antibodies: _____

_____

(b) Explain why this supply is supplemented by antibodies provided in breast milk: _____

_____

Code: A 2

Allergies and Hypersensitivity

Sometimes the immune system may overreact, or react to the wrong substances instead of responding appropriately. This is termed **hypersensitivity** and the immunological response leads to tissue damage rather than immunity. Hypersensitivity reactions occur after a person has been **sensitised** to an antigen. In some cases, this causes only localised discomfort, as in the case of hayfever. More generalised reactions (such as anaphylaxis from insect venom or drug injections), or localised reactions that affect essential body systems (such as asthma), can cause death through asphyxiation and/or circulatory shock.

Hypersensitivity

A person becomes **sensitised** when they form antibodies to harmless substances in the environment such as pollen or spores (steps 1-2 right). These substances, termed **allergens**, act as antigens to induce antibody production and an allergic response. Once a person is sensitised, the antibodies respond to further encounters with the allergen by causing the release of **histamine** from mast cells (steps 4-5). It is histamine that mediates the symptoms of hypersensitivity reactions such as hay fever and asthma. These symptoms include wheezing and airway constriction, inflammation, itching and watering of the eyes and nose, and/or sneezing.

Eyewire

Pollen SEM **Ragweed**

Hay fever (allergic rhinitis) is an allergic reaction to airborne substances such as dust, moulds, pollens, and animal fur or feathers. Allergy to wind-borne pollen is the most common, and certain plants (e.g. ragweed and privet) are highly allergenic. There appears to be a genetic susceptibility to hay fever, as it is common in people with a family history of eczema, hives, and/or asthma. The best treatment for hay fever is to avoid the allergen, although anti-histamines, decongestants, and steroid nasal sprays will assist in alleviating symptoms.

Asthma is a common disease affecting more than three million people in the UK alone. It usually occurs as a result of a reaction to allergens such as house dust and the faeces of house dust mites, pollen, and animal dander. As with all hypersensitivity reactions, it involves the production of histamines from mast cells (far right). The site of the reaction is the respiratory bronchioles where the histamine causes constriction of the airways, accumulation of fluid and mucus, and inability to breathe. During an attack, sufferers show laboured breathing with overexpansion of the chest cavity (photo, right).

Asthma attacks are often triggered by environmental factors such as cold air, exercise, air pollutants, and viral infections. Recent evidence has also indicated the involvement of a bacterium: *Chlamydia pneumoniae*, in about half of all cases of asthma in susceptible adults.

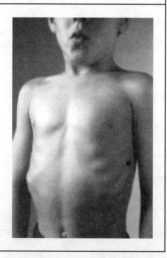

The Basis of Hypersensitivity

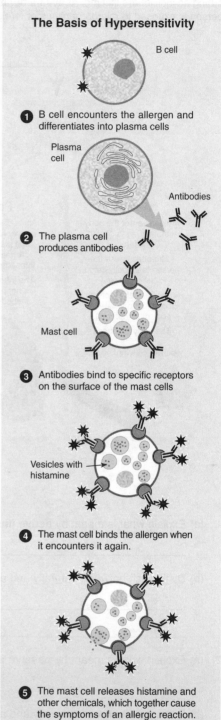

B cell

1 B cell encounters the allergen and differentiates into plasma cells

Plasma cell

Antibodies

2 The plasma cell produces antibodies

Mast cell

3 Antibodies bind to specific receptors on the surface of the mast cells

Vesicles with histamine

4 The mast cell binds the allergen when it encounters it again.

5 The mast cell releases histamine and other chemicals, which together cause the symptoms of an allergic reaction.

1. Explain the role of histamine in hypersensitivity responses: _____

_____

2. Explain what is meant by becoming **sensitised** to an allergen: _____

_____

3. Explain the effect of **bronchodilators** and explain why they are used to treat asthma: _____

_____

Autoimmune Diseases

Any of numerous disorders, including **rheumatoid arthritis**, insulin dependent **diabetes mellitus**, and **multiple sclerosis**, are caused by an individual's immune system reaction to their own cells or tissues. The immune system normally distinguishes self from non-self. Some lymphocytes are capable of reacting against self, but these are generally suppressed. **Autoimmune diseases** occur when there is some interruption of the normal control process, allowing lymphocytes to escape from suppression, or when there is an alteration in some body tissue so that it is no longer recognised as self. The exact mechanisms behind autoimmune malfunctions are not fully understood but pathogens or drugs may play a role in triggering an autoimmune response in someone who already has a genetic predisposition. The reactions are similar to those that occur in allergies, except that in autoimmune disorders, the the hypersensitivity response is to the body itself, rather than to an outside substance.

Multiple Sclerosis

MS is a progressive inflammatory disease of the central nervous system in which scattered patches of **myelin** (white matter) in the brain and spinal cord are destroyed. Myelin is the fatty connective tissue sheath surrounding conducting axons and its destruction results in the symptoms of MS: numbness, tingling, muscle weakness and **paralysis**.

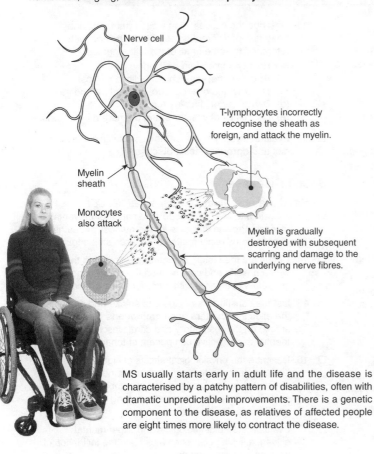

Nerve cell

T-lymphocytes incorrectly recognise the sheath as foreign, and attack the myelin.

Myelin sheath

Monocytes also attack

Myelin is gradually destroyed with subsequent scarring and damage to the underlying nerve fibres.

MS usually starts early in adult life and the disease is characterised by a patchy pattern of disabilities, often with dramatic unpredictable improvements. There is a genetic component to the disease, as relatives of affected people are eight times more likely to contract the disease.

Other Immune System Disorders

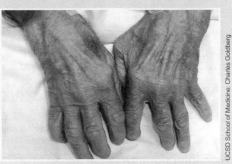

UCSD School of Medicine: Charles Goldberg

Rheumatoid arthritis is a type of joint inflammation, usually in the hands and feet, which results in destruction of cartilage and painful, swollen joints. The disease often begins in adulthood, but can also occur in children or the elderly. Rheumatoid arthritis affects more women than men and is treated with anti-inflammatory and immunosuppressant drugs, and physiotherapy.

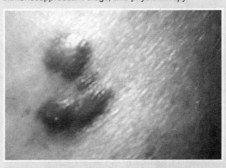

CDC

Lacking a sufficient immune response is called **immune deficiency**, and may be either **congenital** (present at birth) or **acquired** as a result of drugs, cancer, or infectious agents (e.g. HIV infection). HIV causes AIDS, which results in a steady destruction of the immune system. Sufferers then succumb to opportunistic infections and rare cancers such as Kaposi's sarcoma (above).

Defence & the Immune System

1. Explain the basis of the following autoimmune diseases:

   (a) Multiple sclerosis: _____

   _____

   (b) Rheumatoid arthritis: _____

   _____

2. Suggest why autoimmune diseases are difficult to treat effectively: _____

   _____

   _____

3. Explain why sufferers of immune deficiencies, such as AIDS, develop a range of debilitating infections:

   _____

   _____

Non-Infectious Disease

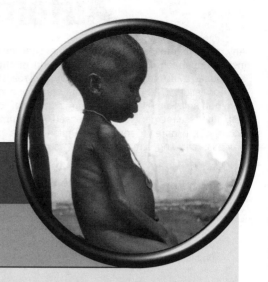

The nature and range of non-infectious disease

Health vs disease: genetic, degenerative, nutritional , and social diseases (including the effects of tobacco and substance abuse).

Learning Objectives

☐ 1. Compile your own glossary from the **KEY WORDS** displayed in **bold type** in the learning objectives below.

Non-infectious Disease *(page 28, 31, 53)*

☐ 2. Explain what is meant by a **non-infectious disease**. Identify and classify examples of non-infectious diseases as: • Nutritional (deficiency) diseases • Genetic (congenital) diseases • Environmental (social) diseases • Mental diseases • Degenerative diseases • Diseases of physiological malfunction e.g. enzyme and hormonal disorders • Autoimmune diseases.

☐ 3. Recognise that diseases may result from a combination of environmental, hereditary, and biological factors.

☐ 4. Using an named example of a non-infectious disease, identify and describe the main features of **epidemiology**.

☐ 5. Identify causes of non-infectious diseases, using an example from each of: **inherited disease**, **nutritional deficiency**, and **social disease**. You may wish to use the examples described below (#6-28).

Genetic Diseases *(pages 45-48)*

☐ 6. Explain what is meant by a **genetic disease**. Name some genetic diseases, and describe their symptoms and their origin (genetic basis). Examples could include:
   (a) **Sickle cell disease**
   (b) **Cystic fibrosis**
   (c) **Huntington disease**
   (d) Trisomic disorders, such as **Down syndrome**

☐ 7. Explain what is meant by the **maternal age effect**. Describe an example of a chromosomal disorder that shows a maternal age effect.

Degenerative Diseases *(pages 33-34, 43)*

☐ 8. Identify the physiological basis of **ageing**. Describe measures to delay the onset of degenerative disease and evaluate their effectiveness.

☐ 9. Describe some of the **degenerative diseases** of ageing, including their symptoms and physiological basis. Include reference to any of the following:
   (a) **Alzheimer's disease** (senile dementia)
   (b) **Osteoarthritis**
   (c) **Osteoporosis**
   (d) **Cataracts** and **hypermetropia** (far-sightedness)

Nutritional Diseases *(pages 38-40, 89-90)*

☐ 10. Explain clearly what is meant by a **nutritional disease**. Distinguish between **starvation**, **malnutrition**, and **deficiency disease** (e.g. vitamin of mineral deficiency).

☐ 11. Describe the causes, diagnosis, symptoms, and treatment of different types of **malnutrition** with reference to some or all of the following:
   (a) Energy and protein deficiency
   (b) **Anorexia nervosa** and/or bulimia nervosa
   (c) **Obesity** and/or excessive intake of fat and salt
   (d) Deficiency of vitamins A and D
   (e) Deficiency of vitamin C and (named) mineral ions.

☐ 12. Evaluate the evidence for the possible links between diet and **coronary heart disease**.

Social Diseases

Smoking and disease *(pages 29-30, 35)*

☐ 13. Explain the role of **tobacco** as a cause of preventable disease. Provide statistics for the number of deaths directly or indirectly related to tobacco smoking.

☐ 14. Document the history of cigarette smoking in the western world and comment on the addictiveness of cigarettes compared with other forms of tobacco.

☐ 15. List the constituents of cigarette smoke and describe the effects of the **tars** and **carcinogens** in tobacco smoke on the respiratory and cardiovascular systems. Identify the addictive component of tobacco.

☐ 16. Describe the physiological effects of cigarette smoking. List and describe the symptoms of some diseases directly or indirectly associated with tobacco smoking: chronic **bronchitis**, **emphysema**, **lung cancer**, and **cardiovascular disease**.

☐ 17. Evaluate the epidemiological and experimental evidence linking cigarette smoking to the incidence of disease and early death.

☐ 18. Describe the short and long term effects of cigarette smoking and list the factors that increase its harmful effects. Describe what is meant by **passive smoking** and comment on its effects on non-smokers. Describe the detrimental health effects of smoking in pregnancy.

Drug abuse *(page 44)*

☐ 19. Define the terms: **drug** and **drug abuse**. Distinguish between recreational drugs, medicinal drugs, and food supplements (e.g. vitamins, bee pollen, spirulina).

☐ 20. Describe the derivation, active ingredient, and physiological effects of some commonly used drugs.

Physiological Malfunction with Multiple Causes

Diabetes mellitus *(pages 41-42, 86)*

☐ 21. Distinguish between **Type I** (juvenile onset) and **Type II** (adult onset) **diabetes mellitus**. Explain their causes, symptoms, severity, and treatment.

☐ 22. Contrast the treatment for juvenile onset diabetes with the treatment for adult onset diabetes.

Cardiovascular disease *(pages 29, 31-32, 111)*

☐ 23. Recognise the term **cardiovascular disease** (CVD), as a broad term encompassing a variety of diseases. Distinguish between some of the different forms of CVD, e.g. **atherosclerosis** and **hypertension**.

☐ 24. Outline stages in the development of **atherosclerosis**. Describe the factors implicated in the development of atherosclerosis e.g. tobacco smoking, lack of exercise, **obesity**, high blood pressure, poor dietary habits.

☐ 25. Describe the **epidemiology** of cardiovascular diseases, particularly coronary heart disease. Relate their global pattern of occurrence to lifestyle factors.

Cancers *(pages 35-37)*

☐ 26. Define the terms **cancer, tumour,** and **carcinogen**. Discuss some of the known causes of cancers and their effects. Recognise the involvement of environmental, hereditary, and biological factors in the development of cancers.

☐ 27. Distinguish between **benign** and **malignant tumours**. Explain why some cancers spread (undergo **metastasis**) more rapidly than others.

☐ 28. Provide details of the development, **symptoms, diagnosis, treatment,** and **prognosis** for one type of cancer. Consider the effectiveness of treatments generally available for cancer. Discuss the role of early detection in more effective cancer control.

Supplementary Texts

See page 7 for additional details of this text:

■ Fullick, A., 2000. **Human Health and Disease** (Heinemann), chpt. 1, 3-6.

■ Murray, P. & N. Owens, 2001. **Behaviour and Populations** (Collins), chpt. 8.

Periodicals

See page 7 for details of publishers of periodicals:

STUDENT'S REFERENCE

Non-infectious causes of cancer

Note that infectious agents are increasingly implicated in the development of cancers.

■ **What is Cancer?** Biol. Sci. Rev., 11(1) Sept. 1998, pp. 38-41. *The cellular basis of cancer, with a look at some new ways to combat the disease.*

■ **Cancer: What is it and how is it Treated?** Biol. Sci. Rev., 16(1) Sept. 2003, pp. 26-30. *An account of the characteristics of cancer, how it arises, and strategies in cancer treatment.*

■ **Out of Control - Unlocking the Genetic Secrets of Cancer** Biol. Sci. Rev., 11(3) January 1999, pp. 38-41. *A look at the failures in gene regulation that lead to the development of cancer.*

■ **Rebels without a Cause** New Scientist, 13 July 2002, (Inside Science). *The causes of cancer: the uncontrolled division of cells that results in tumour formation. Breast cancer is the case study given.*

Cardiovascular & respiratory diseases

■ **Heart Attacks** New Scientist , 12 June 1993, (Inside Science). *The nature of heart attacks and the epidemiology of heart disease.*

■ **Heart Disease and Cholesterol** Biol. Sci. Rev., 13(2) Nov. 2000, pp. 2-5. *The links between dietary fat, cholesterol level, and heart disease.*

■ **Environmental Lung Disease** New Scientist, 23 September 1995 (Inside Science). *Diseases of the lungs and cardiovascular system.*

■ **Smoking** Biol. Sci. Rev. 10(1) Sept. 1997, pp. 14-16. *The effects on human physiology of tobacco smoking, including the types and symptoms of smoking related diseases.*

Health & Disease

Presentation MEDIA to support this topic:

Health & Disease CD-ROM:
• Set 1: The Nature of Disease
• Set 3: Non-Infectious Disease

■ **Why are we so Fat?** National Geographic, 206(2), August 2004, pp. 46-61. *A comprehensive account of the obesity in America and around the world. Includes a summary of health problems associated with obesity and a rather alarming cross section through an obese person.*

Dietary and metabolic diseases

■ **Lactose Intolerance** Biol. Sci. Rev., 17(3), Feb. 2005, pp. 28-31. *The nature of lactose intolerance (the inability to digest milk). Rather than an allergy, this disorder is a physiological response following a genetically programmed loss of lactase.*

■ **Leptin** Biol. Sci. Rev., 15(3), Feb. 2003, pp. 30-32. *The role of the hormone leptin in regulating body mass and controlling obesity.*

■ **Diabetes** Biol. Sci. Rev., 15(2) November 2002, pp. 30-35. *The nature of Type I diabetes: symptoms, complications, monitoring and control of the disease. This account includes details of the structure of the endocrine portion of the pancreas.*

■ **Obesity: A Weighty Problem** Biol. Sci. Rev., 10(1) Sept. 1997, pp. 17-20. *Human diet, the energy intake equation, and an examination of the genetic and environmental causes of obesity.*

■ **Eating Disorders: Myths and Misconceptions** Biol. Sci. Rev., 9(5) May 1997, pp. 25-27. *The causes and treatments of eating disorders.*

■ **Vital Vitamins** Biol. Sci. Rev., 11(5) May 1999, pp. 32-35. *The role of vitamins in the diet, including the diseases caused by vitamin deficiencies.*

■ **Hard Cheese** New Scientist, 15 December 2001, pp. 42-45. *It seems that the modern 'healthy' diet may be bad for bone development and maintenance, accelerating degenerative disease.*

■ **How to Defy Death** New Scientist, 25 March 2000, pp. 20-23. *How can diet promote longevity? Eating less may slow cellular damage.*

■ **Food Glorious Food** New Scientist, 18 Oct. 1997, (Inside Science). *Protective and high risk foods, the role of carbohydrates and fibre and aspects of diet-related health and disease.*

Degenerative diseases

■ **The Biology of Ageing** Biol. Sci. Rev., 10(3) January 1998, pp. 18-21. *Ageing and degenerative disease (includes Alzheimer's and its pathology).*

■ **Unravelling the Mysteries of Human Ageing** Biol. Sci. Rev., 14(3) February 2002, pp. 33-37. *The physiology of human ageing and an account of age related diseases and disabilities.*

■ **Aging** National Geographic, 192(5), Nov. 1997, pp. 2-31. *An account of the physiological aspects of aging as well as the social issues of elderly care.*

■ **Age - Old Story** New Scientist, 23 Jan. 1999, (Inside Science). *The processes involved in aging. An accessible, easy-to-read, but thorough account*

TEACHER'S REFERENCE

■ **Everyday Exposure to Toxic Pollutants** Scientific American, Feb. 1998, pp. 72-77. *How toxic pollutants, chemicals, and air pollution pose a risk of cancer, allergies, and respiratory diseases.*

■ **The Cancer Revolution** New Scientist, 23 August 2003, pp. 36-39. *The use of DNA microarrays to identify the genes responsible for causing cancer. Gene activity signatures could then be used to predict whether a tumour is likely to spread to other parts of the body.*

■ **Untangling the Roots of Cancer** New Scientist, July 2003, pp. 48-57. *How do cells become malignant? This article includes a diagram to explain theories of cancer development.*

■ **What You Need to Know About Cancer** SPECIAL ISSUE: Scientific American, Sept. 1996, entire issue. *Thorough coverage of the genetic and environmental causes of various cancers: symptoms, prevention, detection, and therapies.*

■ **Obesity: An Overblown Epidemic?** Scientific American, June 2005, pp. 48-55. *Arguments for and against the conventional wisdom linking obesity to increased incidence of disease.*

■ **Atherosclerosis: The New View** Scientific American, May 2002, pp. 28-37. *The latest views on the pathological development and rupture of plaques in atherosclerosis. Excellent.*

■ **Dark Angel** New Scientist, 18 Dec. 2004, pp. 38-41. *An account of the p53 gene and the role of its expressed protein in the prevention and triggering of cancers.*

■ **Piecing Together Alzheimer's** Sci. American, Dec. 2000, pp. 52-59. *An excellent account of the physiology and pathology of this common disease.*

■ **Alcohol in the Western World** Scientific American, June 1998, pp. 62-67. *The changing perception of alcohol throughout western civilisation, with a look at the effects on human physiology of excessive alcohol intake.*

■ **Gaining on Fat** Scientific American, August 1996, pp. 70-76. *Discovering the biological roots of obesity and the hope of new treatments.*

Internet

See pages 4-5 for details of how to access **Bio Links** from our web site: **www.thebiozone.com** From Bio Links, access sites under the topics:

HEALTH & DISEASE: • CDC disease links • NewsFile • WHO/OMS: health topics > **Non-Infectious Diseases:** • Asthma • Chemicals and human health • Your genes: your health • FAQ about diabetes • Smoking and your digestive system • Breast cancer screening • Cancer • Cancer Research UK • NCI's Cancernet • Cardiology compass • Heart disease *.. and many others* > **Human Health Issues:** • Eating disorders • British Nutrition Foundation • The effects of drugs on the human body *... and others*

GENETICS > Mutations and Genetic Disorders: Blazing a genetic trail • Your genes: your health • Cystic fibrosis • PKU fact sheet • Facts about cystic fibrosis... *and others*

Non-infectious Disease

Health vs Disease

Disease is more difficult to define than **health**, which is described as a state of complete physical, mental, and social well-being. A disease is usually associated with particular **symptoms** that help to define and diagnose it. The term **disease** is used to describe a condition whereby part or all of an organism's normal physiological function is upset. All diseases, with the exception of some mental diseases, can be classified as **physical diseases** (i.e. diseases that cause permanent or temporary damage to the body). Physical diseases can be subdivided into two major groups: **infectious diseases** caused by an infectious agent (**pathogen**) and **non-infectious diseases** (most of which are better described as disorders). Non-infectious diseases are often not clearly the result of any single factor, but they can be further categorised into major subgroups according to their principal cause (outlined below). However, many diseases fall into more than one category, e.g. Alzheimer's disease and some cancers.

The Nature of Disease

Infectious Diseases

Infectious diseases are diseases that are caused by pathogens and which can be transmitted from one person to another. Most, although not all, pathogens are microorganisms, and they fall into five main categories: viruses, bacteria, fungi, protozoans, and multicellular parasites.

Mental Disorders

The term mental disorder encompasses a range of diseases that affect a person's thoughts, memory, emotions, and personal behaviour. Examples include Alzheimer's, schizophrenia, and depression.

Deficiency Diseases

Deficiency diseases are non-infectious diseases caused by an inadequate or unbalanced diet, or by over eating. Examples include obesity, rickets, scurvy, marasmus, and kwashiorkor.

Degenerative Diseases

Degenerative diseases are non-infectious diseases caused by ageing and the inability of the body to carry out effective repairs and regeneration. Examples include osteoarthritis, Alzheimer's disease, and many cancers.

Social Diseases

Social diseases include a wide range of disorders that are influenced by living conditions and personal behaviour. They may or may not be caused by an infectious agent. Examples include obesity, sexually transmitted diseases, and lung cancer and emphysema due to smoking.

Inherited Diseases

Some diseases result from inherited malfunctions in a body system and have no external cause. Defective genes may cause the failure of a body system throughout a person's life, or the onset of disease may occur later in life. Examples include cystic fibrosis, multiple sclerosis, Alzheimer's, and Huntington's disease.

Down syndrome is a congenital disease caused by having three copies of chromosome 21.

Smoking is a common social behaviour that causes lung cancer, chronic bronchitis, and emphysema.

Mental diseases encompass a range of often unrelated disorders involving disturbances to personality.

Asthma is a common, non-infectious respiratory disease with a number of underlying causes.

1. Discuss the differences between health and disease: _____

_____

_____

_____

2. Using illustrative examples, suggest why many diseases fall into more than one disease category: _____

_____

_____

Diseases Caused by Smoking

Tobacco smoking has only recently been accepted as a major health hazard, despite its practice in developed countries for more than 400 years, and much longer elsewhere. Cigarettes became popular at the end of World War I because they were cheap, convenient, and easier to smoke than pipes and cigars. They remain popular for the further reason that they are more addictive than other forms of tobacco. The milder smoke can be more readily inhaled, allowing **nicotine** (a powerful addictive poison) to be quickly absorbed into the bloodstream. **Lung cancer** is the most widely known and most harmful effect of smoking. Tobacco smoking is also directly associated with coronary artery disease, emphysema, chronic bronchitis, peripheral vascular disease, and stroke. Despite recent indications that smoking-related mortality may be declining in developed countries, one third of all deaths from cancer, including around 90% of lung cancer deaths, are linked to this cause. The damaging components of cigarette smoke include tar, carbon monoxide, nitrogen dioxide, and nitric oxide. Many of these chemicals occur in greater concentrations in sidestream smoke (**passive smoking**) than in mainstream smoke (inhaled) due to the presence of a filter in the cigarette.

Long term effects of tobacco smoking

Smoking damages the arteries of the brain and may result in a **stroke**.

All forms of tobacco-smoking increase the risk of **mouth cancer, lip cancer**, and **cancer of the throat** (pharynx).

Lung cancer is the best known harmful effect of smoking.

In a young man who smokes 20 cigarettes a day, the risk of **coronary artery disease** is increased by about three times over that of a nonsmoker.

Smoking leads to severe constriction of the arteries supplying blood to the extremities and leads to **peripheral vascular disease**.

Short term effects of tobacco smoking

- Reduction in capacity of the lungs.
- Increase in muscle tension and a decrease in steadiness of the hands.
- Raised blood pressure (10-30 points).
- Very sharp rise in carbon monoxide levels in the lungs contributing to breathlessness.
- Increase in pulse rate by up to 20 beats per minute.
- Surface blood vessel constriction drops skin temperature by up to 5°C.
- Dulling of appetite as well as the sense of smell and taste.

How smoking damages the lungs

Non-smoker

Normal alveoli arrangement

Thin layer of mucus

Cilia

Cells lining airways

Smoker

Coalesced alveoli

Extra mucus produced

Smoke particles

Cancerous cell

Smoke particles indirectly destroy the walls of the lung's alveoli.

Cavities lined by heavy black tar deposits.

SPECIMEN A-73-309 DATE

Gross pathology of lung tissue from a patient with emphysema. Tobacco tar deposits can be seen. Tar contains at least 17 known carcinogens.

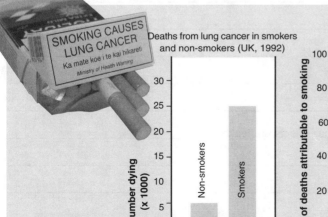

SMOKING CAUSES LUNG CANCER
Ka mate koe i te kai hikareti
Ministry of Health Warning

Deaths from lung cancer in smokers and non-smokers (UK, 1992)

Number dying (x 1000)

Non-smokers / Smokers

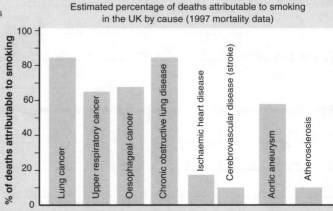

Estimated percentage of deaths attributable to smoking in the UK by cause (1997 mortality data)

% of deaths attributable to smoking

Lung cancer / Upper respiratory cancer / Oesophageal cancer / Chronic obstructive lung disease / Ischaemic heart disease / Cerebrovascular disease (stroke) / Aortic aneurysm / Atherosclerosis

Non-infectious Disease

Code: RDA 2

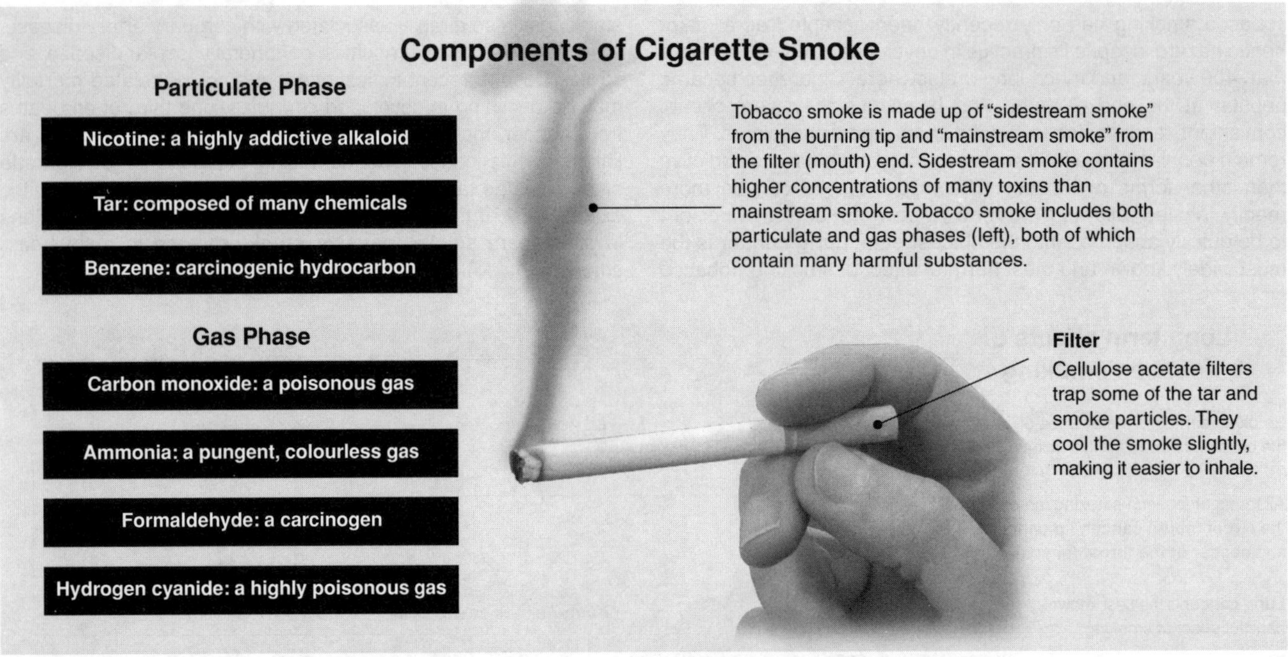

Components of Cigarette Smoke

Particulate Phase

Nicotine: a highly addictive alkaloid

Tar: composed of many chemicals

Benzene: carcinogenic hydrocarbon

Gas Phase

Carbon monoxide: a poisonous gas

Ammonia: a pungent, colourless gas

Formaldehyde: a carcinogen

Hydrogen cyanide: a highly poisonous gas

Tobacco smoke is made up of "sidestream smoke" from the burning tip and "mainstream smoke" from the filter (mouth) end. Sidestream smoke contains higher concentrations of many toxins than mainstream smoke. Tobacco smoke includes both particulate and gas phases (left), both of which contain many harmful substances.

Filter
Cellulose acetate filters trap some of the tar and smoke particles. They cool the smoke slightly, making it easier to inhale.

1. Discuss the physical changes to the lung that result from long-term smoking:

_____

_____

_____

_____

2. Determine the physiological effect of each of the following constituents of tobacco smoke when inhaled:

   (a) Tar: _____

   _____

   (b) Nicotine: _____

   _____

   (c) Carbon monoxide: _____

   _____

3. Describe the symptoms of the following diseases associated with long-term smoking:

   (a) Emphysema: _____

   _____

   (b) Chronic bronchitis: _____

   _____

   (c) Lung cancer: _____

   _____

4. Evaluate the evidence linking cigarette smoking to deleterious effects on health: _____

_____

_____

_____

_____

Cardiovascular Disease

Cardiovascular disease (CVD) is a term describing all diseases involving the heart and blood vessels. It includes coronary heart disease (CHD), atherosclerosis, hypertension (high blood pressure), peripheral vascular disease, stroke, and congenital heart disorders. CVD is responsible for 20% of all deaths worldwide and is the principal cause of deaths in developed countries. Since the 1970s, deaths due to CVD have been declining as a result of better prevention and treatment. Despite this, CVD is still a leading cause of mortality. Its continued prevalence is of considerable public health concern, particularly as many of the **risk factors** involved, including cigarette smoking, obesity, and high blood cholesterol, are controllable. Uncontrollable risk factors include advancing age, gender, and heredity (inherited susceptibility).

Cardiovascular Diseases

Atherosclerosis: Atherosclerosis (sometimes called hardening of the arteries or ischaemic heart disease), is a disease of the arteries caused by **atheroma** (deposits of fats and cholesterol) on the inner walls of the arteries. The lining of the arteries degenerates due to the accumulation of fat and plaques. Atheroma eventually restricts blood flow through the arteries and increases the risk of blood clot formation (**thrombosis**). Complications arising as a result of atherosclerosis include heart attack (**infarction**), stroke and gangrene.

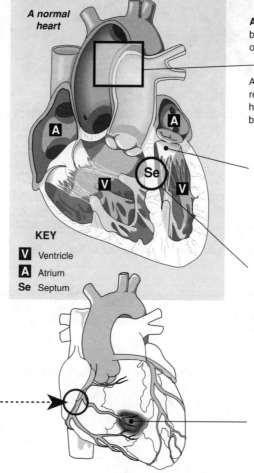

KEY
V Ventricle
A Atrium
Se Septum

A normal heart

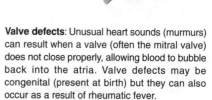

Aortic aneurysm: A ballooning and weakening of the wall of the aorta.

Aneurysms usually result from generalised heart disease and high blood pressure.

Valve defects: Unusual heart sounds (murmurs) can result when a valve (often the mitral valve) does not close properly, allowing blood to bubble back into the atria. Valve defects may be congenital (present at birth) but they can also occur as a result of rheumatic fever.

Septal defects: These hole-in-the-heart congenital defects occur where the dividing wall (**septum**) between the left and right sides of the heart is not closed. These defects may occur between the atria or the ventricles, and are sometimes combined with valve problems.

Myocardial infarction (*heart attack*): Occurs when an area of the heart is deprived of blood supply resulting in tissue damage or death. It is the major cause of death in developed countries. Symptoms of infarction include a sudden onset of chest pain, breathlessness, nausea, and cold clammy skin. Damage to the heart may be so severe that it leads to heart failure and even death (myocardial infarction is fatal within 20 days in 40 to 50% of all cases).

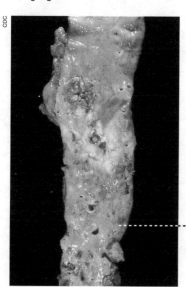

This aorta has been opened lengthwise to reveal the inner surface studded with the lesions of atherosclerosis.

Restricted supply of blood to heart muscle resulting in myocardial infarction

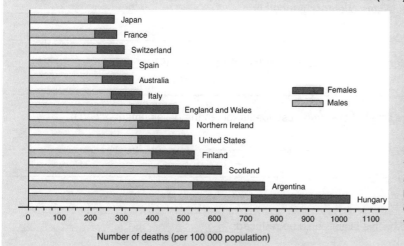

Deaths rates from CVD for males and females from selected countries (2001)

Japan
France
Switzerland
Spain
Australia
Italy
England and Wales
Northern Ireland
United States
Finland
Scotland
Argentina
Hungary

Females
Males

0 100 200 300 400 500 600 700 800 900 1000 1100
Number of deaths (per 100 000 population)

The graph shows the death rate (per 100 000 population) attributable to cardiovascular disease (CVD) in both men and women in selected countries. Data are current to 2001. The rate of CVD is lowest in Japan and France and high in Eastern Europe.

There are many suggested causes for these differences. One study by the World Health Organisation (WHO) stated that variation between countries can be primarily attributed to diet (i.e. saturated fat, salt, vitamin and antioxidant content). The WHO study also found strong north-south gradients in both fruit and vegetable consumption between countries. For example, people in England consumed twice as much fruit and one third more vegetables than those living in Northern Ireland.

Source for data and graph: WHO

Non-infectious Disease

Code: RDA 3

Cardiovascular disease is suspected in people who experience breathlessness, chest pain, or palpitations during exercise, particularly if they also fall into a high-risk category (see table, far right).

Diagnosis of *coronary artery disease* and *angina pectoris* can be made from the results of a **cardiac exercise tolerance test**. During the test, the patient (photo, right) is attached to an electrocardiograph (ECG) machine, which records the electrical activity of the heart during exercise on a treadmill. Angina (chest pain caused by insufficient blood supply to the heart) is confirmed when there are specific changes in the ECG wave patterns as the intensity of exercise is increased.

Diagnosing Cardiovascular Disease

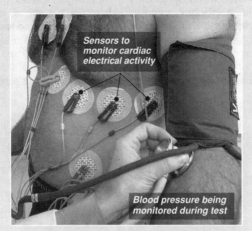

Sensors to monitor cardiac electrical activity

Blood pressure being monitored during test

Risk factors for CVD

- High blood pressure
- Cigarette smoking
- High blood cholesterol
- Obesity
- Type II diabetes mellitus
- High achiever personality
- Environmental stress
- Sedentary lifestyle

Controllable risk factors in the development of cardiovascular disease are listed above. The risks associated with any genetic predisposition to CVD are not included in the list.

1. Explain briefly how atherosclerosis leads to death of heart tissue and a heart attack (infarct): _____
   _____
   _____

2. Mortality attributable to CVD is declining, despite its increasing prevalence. Suggest why: _____
   _____

3. (a) From the graph on the previous page, determine the proportion of CVD deaths occurring in females and males in England and Wales:

   Females: _____   Males: _____

   (b) Suggest a possible reason for this difference: _____
   _____

4. Suggest possible alternative reasons, other than diet, for the global distribution of CVD: _____
   _____
   _____
   _____

5. (a) Distinguish between controllable and uncontrollable risk factors in the development of CVD: _____
   _____
   _____

   (b) Suggest why some of the controllable risk factors often occur together: _____
   _____

   (c) Explain why patients with several risk factors have a much higher risk of developing CVD: _____
   _____

6. (a) Choose one of the controllable risk factors listed above, and describe its role in the development of CVD:
   _____
   _____
   _____

   (b) Suggest how the risk (of CVD) presented by this factor could be reduced: _____
   _____

Degenerative Disease

After attaining physical maturity, the body undergoes a number of **degenerative changes** collectively known as senescence or **ageing**. Ageing results in a progressive failure of the body's homeostatic responses, occurring as a result of cells dying and renewal rates slowing or stopping. It is a general response, producing observable changes in structure and physiology, for example, reduced immune function, a decline in skeletal and muscular strength, and a reduction in the speed of neural processing. Ageing increases susceptibility to stress and disease, and disease and ageing often accelerate together.

Osteoarthritis of the knee joint

Osteoarthritis is a common degenerative disease aggravated by mechanical stress on bone joints. It is characterised by the degeneration of cartilage and the formation of osteophytes (bony outgrowths at the joint). This leads to pain, stiffness, inflammation, and full or partial loss of joint function. Osteoarthritis occurs in almost all people over the age of 60 and affects three times as many women as men. Weight bearing joints such as those in the knee, foot, hips, and spine are most commonly affected. Currently there is no cure for osteoarthritis, although symptoms can be relieved by painkillers and anti-inflammatory drugs.

Loss of lubricating fluid and cartilage

Osteophytes

Osteoporosis of the spine

Osteoporosis is an age-related disorder where bone mass decreases, and there is a loss of height and an increased tendency for bones to break (fracture). Women are at greater risk of developing the disease than men because their skeletons are lighter and their oestrogen levels fall after menopause (oestrogen provides some protection against bone loss). Younger women with low hormone levels and/or low body weight are also affected. Osteoporosis affects the whole skeleton, but especially the spine, hips, and legs.

Loss of height

Hunching of spine

RA

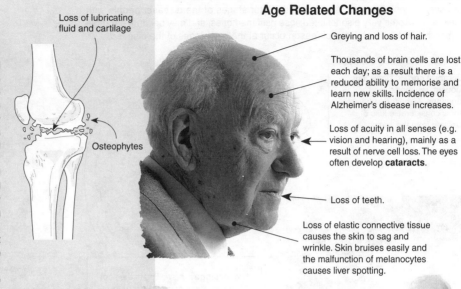

Age Related Changes

Greying and loss of hair.

Thousands of brain cells are lost each day; as a result there is a reduced ability to memorise and learn new skills. Incidence of Alzheimer's disease increases.

Loss of acuity in all senses (e.g. vision and hearing), mainly as a result of nerve cell loss. The eyes often develop **cataracts**.

Loss of teeth.

Loss of elastic connective tissue causes the skin to sag and wrinkle. Skin bruises easily and the malfunction of melanocytes causes liver spotting.

- Several cell types, including neurones, and skeletal and cardiac muscle cells cannot be replaced.
- Metabolic rate decreases. Digestive and kidney function declines.
- The arteries develop deposits associated with atherosclerosis.
- Muscle and bone mass decrease and fat deposits increase. There is a loss of height.
- Arthritis and other joint problems occur, particularly in the hands, feet, hips, elbows, and knees.
- Fertility declines. In women this happens with menopause, usually at about 45-55 years of age. In men, fertility declines more slowly.
- Cancers increase, e.g. prostate cancer in men, and breast and cervical cancer in women.

RA

1. Briefly explain what causes ageing of the body, carefully relating the physiological changes to the observable effects:

_____

_____

_____

2. Name and describe two degenerative diseases or disorders, including reference to symptoms and physiological causes:

(a) _____

_____

_____

_____

Non-infectious Disease

Code: RA 2

The Malfunctioning Brain:
The Effects of Alzheimer's Disease

Alzheimer's disease is a disabling neurological disorder affecting about 5% of the population over 65. Its causes are largely unknown, its effects are irreversible, and it has no cure. Sufferers of Alzheimer's have trouble remembering recent events and they become confused and forgetful. In the later stages of the disease, people with Alzheimer's become very disoriented, lose past memories, and may become paranoid and moody. Dementia and loss of reason occur at the end stages of the disease.

Upper Brain	Lower Brain
Normal	

Early Alzheimer's

Late Alzheimer's

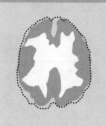 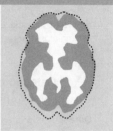

Cerebral cortex: Conscious thought, reasoning, and language. Alzheimer's sufferers show considerable loss of function from this region.

Hippocampus: A swelling in the floor of the lateral ventricle. It contains complex foldings of the cortical tissue and is involved in the establishment of memory patterns. In Alzheimer's sufferers, it is one of the first regions to show loss of neurones and accumulation of amyloid.

It is not uncommon for Alzheimer's sufferers to wander and become lost and disorientated.

Alzheimer's is associated with accelerated loss of neurones, particularly in regions of the brain that are important for memory and intellectual processing, such as the cerebral cortex and hippocampus. The disease has been linked to abnormal accumulations of protein-rich **amyloid** plaques, which invade the brain tissue and interfere with synaptic transmission. The brain scans above show diminishing brain function in certain areas of the brain in Alzheimer's sufferers. Note, particularly in the two lower scans, how much the brain has shrunk (original size indicated by the dotted line). Light areas indicate brain activity.

(b) _____
_____
_____
_____
_____
_____

3. Suggest how weight-bearing exercise could delay the onset of ageing: _____
_____
_____
_____

4. Some loss of neuronal function occurs normally as a result of ageing. Identify the features distinguishing Alzheimer's disease from normal age related loss of neuronal function:
_____
_____
_____

Cancer

Cancer is a term describing a large group of diseases characterised by the progressive and uncontrolled growth of abnormal cells. Cancer is not a new disease, nor is it restricted just to humans. Most other animals suffer from cancer; evidence of it has even been found in the fossilised bones of dinosaurs. There is no single cause for all the forms of cancer; environmental, genetic, and biological factors may all be involved. Although the incidence of cancer has apparently increased in more recent times, this may simply reflect our increased life spans, as the incidence of many cancers increases with age. Of all cancer deaths, nearly half are caused by just four cancers (lung, bowel, breast, and prostate).

Features of Cancer Cells

The bloated, lumpy shape is readily distinguishable from a healthy cell, which has a flat, scaly appearance.

Metabolism may be deranged and the cell ceases to function.

Cancerous cells lose their attachments to neighbouring cells.

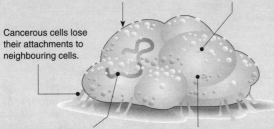

Cancer cells may have unusual numbers of chromosomes.

Cancer cells can go on dividing indefinitely, if they have a continual supply of nutrients, and are said to be immortal.

The diagram *above* shows a single **lung cell** that has become cancerous. It no longer carries out the role of a lung cell, and instead takes on a parasitic 'lifestyle', taking from the body what it needs in the way of nutrients and contributing nothing in return. The rate of cell division is greater than in normal cells in the same tissue because there is no *resting phase* between divisions.

Common Cancers

Skin cancer (melanoma): Cancerous tumours usually develop on skin exposed to **UV light**, but can occur anywhere on the body. Melanomas generally develop from an existing mole, which may enlarge, become lumpy, bleed, change colour, or develop a spreading black edge (as shown below). Melanomas are highly **malignant** and often spread to other parts of the body.

Lung cancer: Lung cancer is one of the most common of all malignant tumours and 98% of all cases are associated with cigarette smoking. Symptoms of lung cancer include coughing up blood, chest pain, breathlessness, and headache if the tumour has metastasised to the brain. These symptoms are generally caused by the tumour impairing lung function.

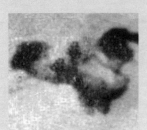

A melanoma with the characteristic spreading black edge.

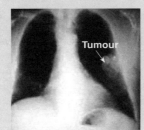

Chest X-ray showing a large, dense mass indicating the presence of a tumour.

Stages in the Formation of Cancer

The growth of a cancer begins when the genes controlling cell growth and multiplication (**oncogenes**) are transformed by agents known as **carcinogens**. Most well studied is the p53 gene which normally acts to prevent cell division in damaged cells. Scientists have found that the p53 gene is altered in 40% of all cancers. Once a cell is transformed into a tumour-forming type (**malignant**), the change in its oncogenes is passed on to all offspring cells:

Cancer cells ignore density-dependent inhibition and continue to multiply even after contacting one another, piling up until the nutrient supply becomes limiting.

1. Benign tumour cells
Defects (mutations) in one or two controlling genes cause the formation of a benign tumour. This is a localised population of proliferating cells where formation of new cells is matched by cell death.

2. Malignant tumour cells
More mutations may cause the cells to become malignant. These cells stop producing a chemical that prevents blood vessels from forming. New capillaries grow into the tumour, providing it with nutrients.

3. Metastasis
The new capillaries also provide a route for the malignant cells to break away from the tumour and travel to other parts of the body where they start new cancers.

Malignant cells break away from tumour mass and travel to other parts of the body either through the **blood system** or **lymphatic system**.

1. Briefly describe the characteristics of the following stages of a developing cancer:

(a) Benign tumour: _____

_____

(b) Malignant tumour: _____

_____

_____

Code: A 2

Cancer Symptoms

The symptoms produced by different kinds of cancers depends on the site of growth, the tissue of origin, and the extent of the growth. Symptoms may be a direct feature of the growth (e.g. lumps), bleeding or disruption of the function of the organ affected.

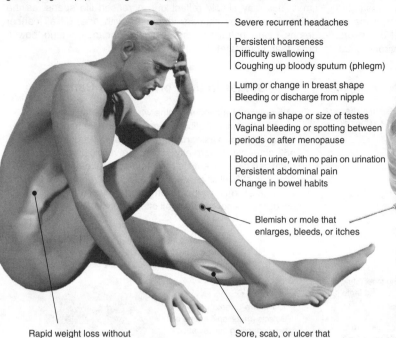

Severe recurrent headaches

Persistent hoarseness
Difficulty swallowing
Coughing up bloody sputum (phlegm)

Lump or change in breast shape
Bleeding or discharge from nipple

Change in shape or size of testes
Vaginal bleeding or spotting between periods or after menopause

Blood in urine, with no pain on urination
Persistent abdominal pain
Change in bowel habits

Blemish or mole that
enlarges, bleeds, or itches

Rapid weight loss without
an apparent cause

Sore, scab, or ulcer that
fails to heal within 3 weeks

Treatment of Cancer

Chemotherapy

Chemotherapy is the treatment of cancer by drugs that act selectively on the cancer cells. Anticancer drugs act either by destroying tumour cells or stopping them from multiplying. Unfortunately, the drugs used in these treatments may also have substantial effects on normal tissue. Chemotherapeutic drugs act on all rapidly dividing cells, not just tumour cells. They may cause destruction of white blood cells, hair loss, sterility, and affect the mouth and intestines.

Radiotherapy

Ionising radiation, normally a source of damage to DNA, is used to treat cancer tumours. As the radiation passes through the diseased tissue, it destroys or slows down the development of abnormal cells. Provided the correct dosage of radiation is given, normal cells suffer very little, and there is no long-term damage. Side effects are usually short-lived and involve minor burning of the skin or some localised hair loss.

(c) Metastasis: _____

_____

2. Explain how the following treatments work to destroy cancerous tumours (while leaving healthy tissue less affected):

(a) Chemotherapy: _____

_____

_____

(b) Radiotherapy: _____

_____

_____

3. (a) Describe some of the unwanted (harmful) side effects of these two treatments (above):

_____

_____

(b) Explain why these side effects happen: _____

_____

4. List the probable causes and characteristic symptoms associated with the following types of cancer:

(a) Causes of skin cancer: _____

Symptoms: _____

_____

(b) Causes of lung cancer: _____

Symptoms: _____

_____

Breast Cancer

Breast cancer is by far the most common cancer in women, affecting more than 1 million women worldwide. More than 25% of all female cancers occur in the breast, and the incidence increases with age, with 80% of cases occurring in post menopausal women. Fewer than 1% of breast cancer cases occur in men. Female sex hormones are implicated in the development of many breast cancers. The incidence of the disease is higher in women who began menstruation early and/ or whose menopause was late. Women who have no children or who had their first child when they were in their late 20s or 30s (or older) are also at higher risk. There is also a definite **familial** (heredity) factor in many cases. A high fat diet is also implicated. In Japan, where a low fat diet is typical, the disease is rare. Yet Japanese women living in the United States and eating a higher-fat American diet have the same rate of breast cancer as American women generally.

Characteristics of breast cancer

The incidence of breast cancer increases with age; it is almost unknown before age 25 but the incidence rises sharply in women aged 25-44. Most deaths from breast cancer occur because the disease has already spread beyond the breast when first detected.

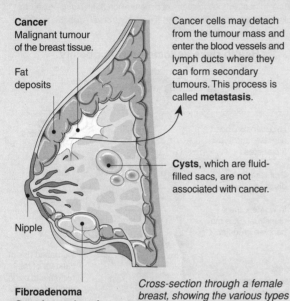

Cancer
Malignant tumour of the breast tissue.

Fat deposits

Nipple

Fibroadenoma
One of a number of common benign tumours.

Cancer cells may detach from the tumour mass and enter the blood vessels and lymph ducts where they can form secondary tumours. This process is called **metastasis**.

Cysts, which are fluid-filled sacs, are not associated with cancer.

Cross-section through a female breast, showing the various types of tissue masses present.

Breast self examination

Regular self-examinations to detect lumps in the breast tissue are recommended (left). Regular breast self examination may be the first step in detecting abnormal changes in the breast tissue.

Mammography

Mammography, which involves a breast X-ray, can detect tumours less than 15 mm in diameter (too small to be detected by a physical breast exam).

In mammography, the breast is compressed between the X-ray plate below and a plastic cover screen above. Several views are then taken.

A **biopsy** is performed if there is a chance that a lump may be malignant. A sample of the affected tissue is taken with a hollow needle and examined under a microscope. If cancerous cells are present, X-rays, ultrasound scanning, and blood tests can determine if the disease has spread to other parts of the body, such as the bones or the liver. Treatment may then follow.

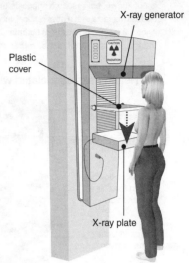

X-ray generator

Plastic cover

X-ray plate

Treatment

Surgical removal of the tumour achieves a cure (as defined by survival for 20 years after treatment) in one third of women with early breast cancer. Studies have shown that survival is not improved by extensive surgery such as radical mastectomy (1). Less radical procedures (2 and 3) are now frequently recommended, combined with **radiotherapy** or **anticancer drugs**, such as *tamoxifen*.

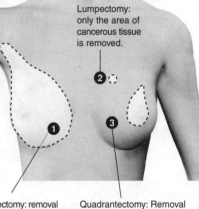

Lumpectomy: only the area of cancerous tissue is removed.

Radical mastectomy: removal of the entire breast, chest muscle, associated lymph nodes, and fat and skin.

Quadrantectomy: Removal of the tumour plus a wedge of surrounding tissue.

1. Describe three factors associated with increased risk of developing breast cancer and suggest why they increase risk:

_____

_____

2. Suggest in what way breast self examination may be deficient in detecting early breast cancers: _____

_____

3. Describe a possible treatment for early breast cancer involving a small isolated tumour: _____

_____

4. State the evidence for a link between diet and increased risk of developing breast cancer: _____

_____

_____

Non-infectious Disease

Code: A 2

Dietary Disorders

Most forms of malnutrition in western societies are the result of poorly balanced nutrient intakes rather than a lack of food *per se*. Dietary disorders may arise as a result of overeating (**obesity**), insufficient food intake (**anorexia nervosa**), or abnormally erratic eating habits (**bulimia nervosa**). Other health problems typically prevalent in western societies, including **cardiovascular diseases**, have been associated to varying degrees with the consumption of highly processed foods, high in cholesterol and saturated fats. Low fibre intake is a factor in the development of **colon cancer**, while high salt intake may lead to **hypertension**.

Anorexia Nervosa

An eating disorder characterized by an intense fear of being fat, severe weight loss, and a wilful avoidance of food. Clinically, anorexics are below 75% of the weight expected for their height and age. Anorexia most often affects teenage girls and young adult women (approximately 5% of sufferers are male). The exact cause of this form of self-starvation is not known, but research suggests that it is caused when emotional distress interacts with a physiological imbalance in a vulnerable individual. Anorexia is quite distinct from **bulimia**. Bulimics generally binge eat, and then purge their stomachs, rather than avoiding food altogether.

Obesity

Obesity is the most common form of malnutrition in affluent societies. It is a condition where there is too much body fat (not the same as being overweight). In Australia, 9% of men and 11% of women are obese. Some genetic and hormonal causes are known, although obesity is a result of energy intake (eating) exceeding the **net energy expenditure**. Dieting is often ineffective for long-term weight loss because once normal eating is resumed the body responds by storing more fat in fat cells. Obesity increases the incidence of hypertension (high blood pressure), stroke, coronary artery disease, and Type II (adult onset) diabetes mellitus.

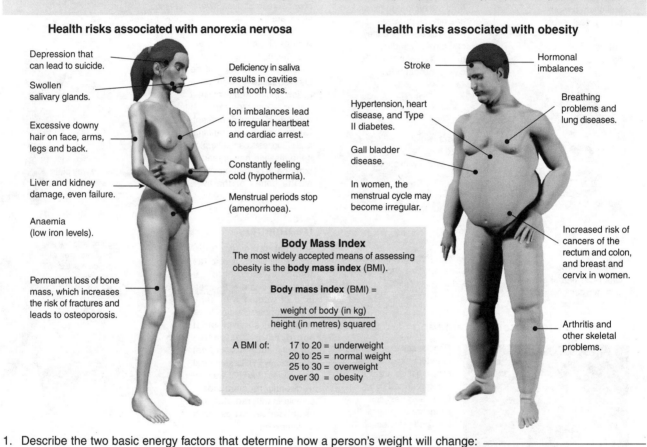

Health risks associated with anorexia nervosa

Depression that can lead to suicide.

Swollen salivary glands.

Excessive downy hair on face, arms, legs and back.

Liver and kidney damage, even failure.

Anaemia (low iron levels).

Permanent loss of bone mass, which increases the risk of fractures and leads to osteoporosis.

Deficiency in saliva results in cavities and tooth loss.

Ion imbalances lead to irregular heartbeat and cardiac arrest.

Constantly feeling cold (hypothermia).

Menstrual periods stop (amenorrhoea).

Health risks associated with obesity

Stroke

Hypertension, heart disease, and Type II diabetes.

Gall bladder disease.

In women, the menstrual cycle may become irregular.

Hormonal imbalances

Breathing problems and lung diseases.

Increased risk of cancers of the rectum and colon, and breast and cervix in women.

Arthritis and other skeletal problems.

Body Mass Index

The most widely accepted means of assessing obesity is the **body mass index** (BMI).

Body mass index (BMI) =

$$\frac{\text{weight of body (in kg)}}{\text{height (in metres) squared}}$$

A BMI of:
- 17 to 20 = underweight
- 20 to 25 = normal weight
- 25 to 30 = overweight
- over 30 = obesity

1. Describe the two basic energy factors that determine how a person's weight will change: _____

_____

2. Using the BMI, calculate the minimum and maximum weight at which a 1.85 m tall man would be considered:

   (a) Overweight: _____   (c) Obese: _____

   (b) Normal weight: _____   (d) Underweight: _____

3. State the possible health consequences of the following aspects of a diet:

   (a) High salt consumption: _____

   (b) Low fibre content: _____

   (c) High cholesterol content: _____

4. Identify the key differences between anorexia nervosa and bulimia nervosa: _____

_____

_____

Deficiency Diseases

Malnutrition is the general term for nutritional disorders resulting from not having enough food (starvation), not enough of the right food (deficiency), or too much food (obesity). Children under 5 are the most at risk from starvation and deficiency diseases because they are growing rapidly and are more susceptible to disease. Malnutrition is a key factor in the deaths of 6 million children each year and, in developing countries, dietary deficiencies are a major problem. In these countries, malnutrition usually presents as **marasmus** or **kwashiorkor** (energy and protein deficiencies).

Specific vitamin and mineral deficiencies (below and following) are often associated with specific diseases, e.g. beriberi (vitamin B_1), scurvy (vitamin C), rickets (vitamin D), pellagra (niacin), or anaemia (iron). Vitamin deficiencies in childhood result in chronic, lifelong disorders. Deficiency diseases are rare in developed countries. People who do suffer from some form of dietary deficiency are either alcoholics, people with intestinal disorders that prevent proper nutrient uptake, or people with very restricted diets (e.g. vegans).

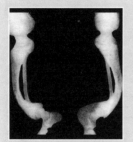

Vitamin D Deficiency

Lack of vitamin D in children produces the disease rickets. In adults a similar disease is called osteomalacia. Suffers typically show skeletal deformities (e.g. bowed legs, left) because inadequate amounts of calcium and phosphorus are incorporated into the bones. Vitamin D is produced by the skin when exposed to sunlight and it is vital for the absorption of calcium from the diet.

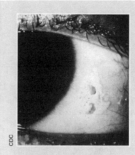

Vitamin A Deficiency

Vitamin A (found in animal livers, eggs, and dairy products) is essential for the production of light-absorbing pigments in the eye and for the formation of cell structures. Symptoms of deficiency include loss of night vision, inflammation of the eye, **keratomalacia** (damage to the cornea), and the appearance of **Bitots spots** – foamy, opaque patches on the white of the eye (refer to photo).

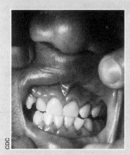

Vitamin C Deficiency

Vitamin C deficiency causes a disease known as scurvy. It is now rare in developed countries because of increased consumption of fresh fruit and vegetables. Inadequate vitamin C intake disturbs the body's normal production of collagen, a protein in connective tissue that holds body structures together. This results in poor wound healing, rupture of small blood vessels (visible bleeding in the skin), swollen gums, and loose teeth.

Vitamin B$_{12}$ Deficiency

Found primarily in meat, but also in eggs and dairy products. B_{12} is required for nucleic acid and protein metabolism, and for the maturation of red blood cells. It is essential for proper growth and for the proper nervous system function. B_{12} deficiency results in **pernicious anaemia**, poor appetite, weight loss, growth failure, tiredness, brain damage, nervousness, muscle twitching, degeneration of the spinal cord, depression, and lack of balance.

Kwashiorkor

A severe type of protein-energy deficiency in young children (1-3 years old), occurring mainly in poor rural areas in the tropics. Kwashiorkor occurs when a child is suddenly weaned on to a diet that is low in calories, protein, and certain essential micronutrients. The problem is often made worse by a poor appetite due to illnesses such as measles. Children have stunted growth, oedema (accumulation of fluid in the tissues), and are inactive, apathetic and weak. Resistance against infection is lost, which may be fatal.

Marasmus

Marasmus is the most common form of deficiency disease. It is a severe form of protein and energy malnutrition that usually occurs in famine or starvation conditions. Children suffering from marasmus are stunted and extremely emaciated. They have loose folds of skin on the limbs and buttocks, due to the loss of fat and muscle tissue. Unlike kwashiorkor sufferers, marasmus does not cause the bloated and elongated abdomen. However sufferers have no resistance to disease and common infections are typically fatal.

1. Distinguish between **malnutrition** and **starvation**: _____

_____

_____

_____

_____

2. For each of the following vitamins, identify the natural sources of the vitamin, its function, and effect of deficiency:

(a) Vitamin A: _____

Function: _____

Deficiency: _____

(b) Vitamin B$_{12}$: _____

Function: _____

Deficiency: _____

Code: RA 2

Non-infectious Disease

Common Mineral Deficiencies

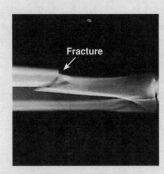 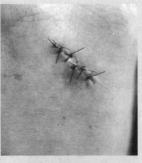 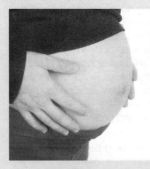 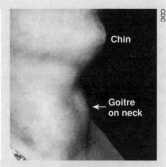

Calcium Deficiency

Calcium is required for enzyme function, formation of bones and teeth, blood clotting, and muscular contraction. Calcium deficiency causes poor bone growth and structure, increasing the tendency of bones to fracture and break. It also results in muscular spasms and poor blood clotting ability.

Zinc Deficiency

Zinc is found in red meat, poultry, fish, whole grain cereals and breads, legumes, and nuts. It is important for enzyme activity, production of insulin, making of sperm, and perception of taste. A deficiency in zinc causes growth retardation, a delay in puberty, muscular weakness, dry skin, and a delay in wound healing.

Iron Deficiency

Anaemia results from lower than normal levels of haemoglobin in red blood cells. Iron from the diet is required to produce haemoglobin. People most at risk include women during **pregnancy** and those with an inadequate dietary intake. Symptoms include fatigue, fainting, breathlessness, and heart palpitations.

Iodine Deficiency

Iodine is essential for the production of thyroid hormones. These hormones control the rate of metabolism, growth, and development. Shortage of iodine in the diet may lead to **goitre** (thyroid enlargement as shown above). Iodine deficiency is also responsible for some cases of thyroid underactivity (**hypothyroidism**).

(c) Vitamin C: _____

   Function: _____

   Deficiency: _____

(d) Vitamin D: _____

   Function: _____

   Deficiency: _____

3. Suggest why young children, pregnant women, and athletes are among the most susceptible to dietary deficiencies:

_____

_____

_____

4. Explain why a lack of iron leads to the symptoms of anaemia (fatigue and breathlessness): _____

_____

_____

5. Suggest why a zinc deficiency is associated with muscular weakness and a delay in puberty: _____

_____

_____

6. Suggest why table salt is often iodised: _____

_____

7. Explain why people suffering from nutritional deficiencies have a poor resistance to disease: _____

_____

_____

_____

_____

Control of Blood Glucose

The endocrine portions of the **pancreas**, specifically the alpha and beta cells of the **islets of Langerhans**, produce two hormones, **insulin** and **glucagon**. Together, these hormones mediate the regulation of blood glucose, maintaining a steady state through **negative feedback**. Insulin promotes a decrease in blood glucose through synthesis of glycogen and cellular uptake of glucose. Glucagon promotes an increase in blood glucose through the breakdown of glycogen and the synthesis of glucose from amino acids. Restoration of normal blood glucose level acts through negative feedback to stop hormone secretion. Regulating blood glucose to within narrow limits allows energy to be available to cells as needed. Extra energy is stored, as glycogen or fat, and is mobilised to meet energy needs as required. The liver is pivotal in these carbohydrate conversions.

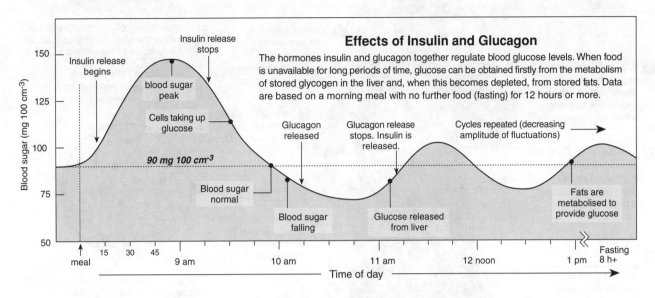

Effects of Insulin and Glucagon

The hormones insulin and glucagon together regulate blood glucose levels. When food is unavailable for long periods of time, glucose can be obtained firstly from the metabolism of stored glycogen in the liver and, when this becomes depleted, from stored fats. Data are based on a morning meal with no further food (fasting) for 12 hours or more.

Negative feedback in the control of blood glucose

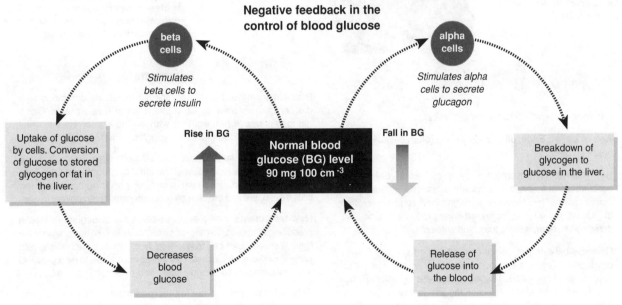

1. (a) Identify the stimulus for the release of insulin: _____

    (b) Identify the stimulus for the release of glucagon: _____

    (c) Explain how glucagon brings about an increase in blood glucose level: _____

    _____

    (d) Explain how insulin brings about a decrease in blood glucose level: _____

    _____

2. Outline the role of negative feedback in the control of blood glucose: _____

    _____

3. Explain why fats are metabolised after a long period without food: _____

    _____

Code: A 2

Non-infectious Disease

Diabetes Mellitus

Diabetes is a general term for a range of disorders sharing two common symptoms: production of large amounts of urine and excessive thirst. Other symptoms depend on the type of diabetes.

Diabetes mellitus is the most common form of diabetes and is characterised by high blood sugar. **Type I** has a juvenile onset while **Type II** affects adults.

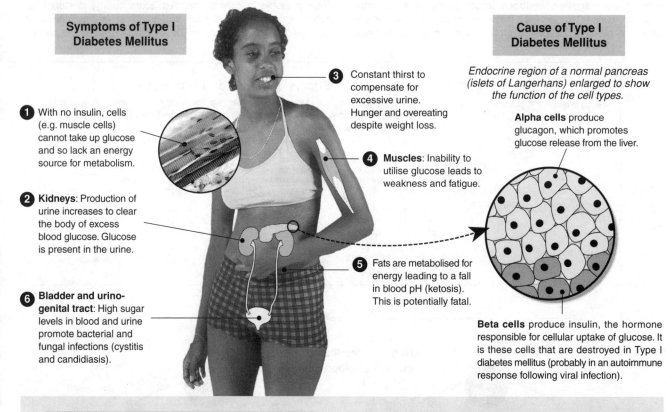

Symptoms of Type I Diabetes Mellitus

1 With no insulin, cells (e.g. muscle cells) cannot take up glucose and so lack an energy source for metabolism.

2 **Kidneys**: Production of urine increases to clear the body of excess blood glucose. Glucose is present in the urine.

6 **Bladder and urino-genital tract**: High sugar levels in blood and urine promote bacterial and fungal infections (cystitis and candidiasis).

3 Constant thirst to compensate for excessive urine. Hunger and overeating despite weight loss.

4 **Muscles**: Inability to utilise glucose leads to weakness and fatigue.

5 Fats are metabolised for energy leading to a fall in blood pH (ketosis). This is potentially fatal.

Cause of Type I Diabetes Mellitus

Endocrine region of a normal pancreas (islets of Langerhans) enlarged to show the function of the cell types.

Alpha cells produce glucagon, which promotes glucose release from the liver.

Beta cells produce insulin, the hormone responsible for cellular uptake of glucose. It is these cells that are destroyed in Type I diabetes mellitus (probably in an autoimmune response following viral infection).

Type I Diabetes mellitus (insulin dependent)

Incidence: About 10-15% of all diabetics.

Age at onset: Early; often in childhood (often called juvenile onset diabetes).

Symptoms: Symptoms are severe. Insulin deficiency accelerates fat breakdown and leads to a number of metabolic complications: hyperglycaemia (high blood sugar), excretion of glucose in the urine, increased urine production, excessive thirst and hunger, weight loss, and ketosis.

Cause: Absolute deficiency of insulin due to lack of insulin production (pancreatic beta cells are destroyed in an autoimmune reaction). There is a genetic component but usually a childhood viral infection triggers the development of the disease. Mumps, coxsackie, and rubella are implicated.

Treatments

Present treatments: Regular insulin injections combined with dietary management to keep blood sugar levels stable. Blood glucose is monitored regularly with testing kits to guard against sudden falls in blood glucose (hypoglycaemia).

Until recently, insulin was extracted from dead animals. Now, genetically engineered yeast or bacterial cells containing the gene for human insulin are grown in culture, providing abundant, low cost insulin, without the side effects associated with animal insulin.

New treatments: Cell therapy involves the transplant of insulin producing islet cells. To date, approximately 400 patients worldwide have received islet cell transplants from donor pancreases, with varying degrees of success. Cell therapy promises to be a practical and effective way to provide sustained relief for Type I diabetics.

Future treatments: In the future, gene therapy, where the gene for insulin is inserted into the diabetic's cells, may be possible.

1. Describe the **symptoms** for diabetes mellitus Type I and relate these to the physiological cause of the disease:

_____

_____

_____

_____

2. Summarise the **treatments** for diabetes mellitus Type I (list key words/phrases only):

   (a) Present treatment: _____

   (b) New treatments: _____

   (c) Future treatments: _____

Visual Defects

The lens of the eye has two convex surfaces (biconvex). When light enters the eye, the lens bends the incoming rays towards each other so that they intersect at the focal point on the central fovea of the retina. By altering the curvature of the lens, the focusing power of the eye can be adjusted. This adjustment of the eye for near or far vision is called **accommodation** and it is possible because of the elasticity of the lens. For some people,

the shape of the eyeball or the lens prevents convergence of the light rays on the central fovea, and images are focused in front of, or behind, the retina. Such visual defects (below) can be corrected with specific lenses. As we age, the lens loses some of its elasticity and, therefore, its ability to accommodate. This inability to focus on nearby objects due to loss of lens elasticity is a natural part of ageing and is called **far sight**.

Normal vision

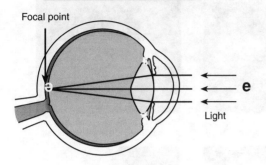

In normal vision, light rays from an object are bent sufficiently by the cornea and lens, and converge on the central fovea. A clear image is formed. Images are focused upside down and mirror reversed on the retina. The brain automatically interprets the image as right way up.

Accommodation for near and distant vision

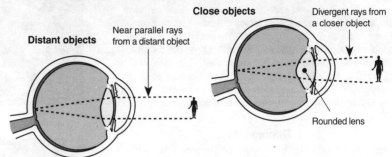

The degree of refraction occurring at each surface of the eye is precise. The light rays reflected from an object 6 m or more away are nearly parallel to one another. Those reflected from near objects are divergent. The light rays must be refracted differently in each case so that they fall exactly on the central fovea. This is achieved through adjustment of the shape of the lens (accommodation). Accommodation from distant to close objects occurs by rounding the lens to shorten its focal length, since the image distance to the object is essentially fixed.

Short sightedness (myopia)

Myopia (top row, right) results from an elongated eyeball or a thickened lens. Left uncorrected, distant objects are focused in front of the retina and appear blurred. To correct myopic vision, concave (negative) lenses are used to move the point of focus backward to the retina. Myopia is not necessarily genetic; it can occur as the result of excessive close work, especially when young, or as a result of living in confined spaces (e.g. people working and living in submarines).

Long sightedness (hypermetropia)

Long sightedness (bottom row, right) results from a shortened eyeball or from a lens that is too thin. Left uncorrected, light is focused behind the retina and near objects appear blurred. Mild or moderate hypermetropia, which occurs naturally in young children, may be overcome by **accommodation**. In more severe cases, corrective lenses are used to bring the point of focus forward to produce a clear image. This is achieved using a convex (positive) lens.

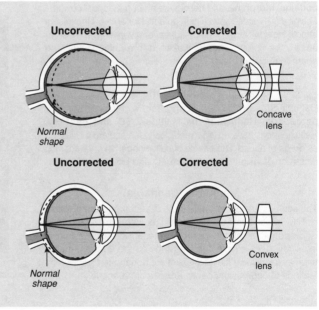

1. With respect to formation of the image, describe what is happening in:

   (a) Short sighted people: _____

   (b) Long sighted people: _____

2. In general terms, describe how the use of lenses corrects the following problems associated with vision:

   (a) Myopia: _____

   (b) Hypermetropia: _____

3. Explain how accommodation of the eye for near and distant vision is achieved: _____

   _____

   _____

Non-infectious Disease

Code: A 2

Substance Abuse

Drugs are substances that alter the functioning of the mind or body. Drug use is divided into medicinal treatments (used to treat a disease or its symptoms) and **recreational drugs** (used to enhance life experiences). Recreational drugs, e.g. marijuana, cocaine, metamphetamines, heroin, LSD, tranquillisers, and alcohol are usually taken for their mind-altering effects. Many recreational drugs are both psychologically and physically **addictive**. Once addicted, a user is unable to function without the drug. Moreover, because of the phenomenon of **drug tolerance**, ever-increasing doses are needed achieve the same effect. When the drug is withdrawn, they suffer **withdrawal** symptoms which can range from mild to life threatening.

Stimulants

These are drugs that stimulate or speed up the central nervous system and give the feeling of increased alertness and physical activity and decreased appetite. Stimulants include **caffeine**, **amphetamines**, and **cocaine** (**crack** is a pure form of cocaine). The effects of chronic use include restlessness, insomnia, psychotic behaviour, stroke, and death. Other effects on the body will depend on how the drug is taken. Regular snorting of cocaine for example, leads to loss of sense of smell, nosebleeds, and difficulty swallowing. Drug injection carries the risk of HIV and severe allergic reactions (anaphylaxis).

Depressants

These are drugs that slow down or suppress the central nervous system. Depressant drugs include **alcohol**, **barbiturates**, and **tranquillisers**. Low doses have a calming effect to the point of promoting sleep. High doses can cause unconsciousness and death.

Analgesics

Analgesics are substances that provide relief from pain. Mild analgesics include paracetemol and aspirin. Opiates, e.g. **codeine**, **morphine**, and **heroin** are among the most powerful analgesics. Opiates have a high potential for abuse. Unpleasant effects include restlessness, nausea, and vomiting. With larger doses, the user cannot be wakened, breathing slows, and death may occur.

Hallucinogens

Hallucinogens (psychedelics), affect a person's sensory perception. Hallucinogens include **LSD** and **ecstasy**. Hallucinogens have no legal medicinal uses and are all classed as drugs of abuse. The effects of hallucinogens vary from mild distortion of vision to intense anxiety and psychosis.

Marijuana (Cannabis)

The active ingredient in marijuana is delta-tetrahydrocannabinol or THC, which binds to cannabinoid receptors in the brain and is responsible for the potency and effects of marijuana intoxication. Its effects begin as soon as the drug enters the brain and include initial feelings of euphoria, often followed by feelings of depression, panic, anxiety, or paranoia.

Drugs and their Effects

Ice metamphetamine with glass pipe through which vapours are inhaled.

Cocaine is an addictive stimulant drug that interferes with dopamine uptake.

Alcohol is a widely used depressant.

Tranquillisers have a calming effect.

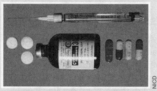

Analgesics, such as codeine (above) are widely used in medicine.

Unlike analgesics, hallucinogens such as **ecstasy** have no medicinal uses.

Cannabis sativa has a variety of uses unrelated to its status as a drug.

Dried marijuana is usually smoked and abuse can lead to lung disease.

1. Explain the difference between **psychological** addiction and **physical** addiction: _____

_____

_____

2. Outline the main effects of a **named** recreational drug: _____

_____

_____

3. Suggest how the use of recreational drugs by a pregnant woman would affect her unborn child: _____

_____

Inherited Metabolic Disorders

Humans have more than 6000 physiological diseases attributed to mutations in single genes and over one hundred syndromes known to be caused by chromosomal abnormality. The number of genetic disorders identified increases every year. The work of the Human Genome Project is enabling the identification of the genetic basis of these disorders. This will facilitate the development of new drug therapies and gene therapies. Four genetic disorders are summarised below.

Sickle Cell Disease	β-Thalassaemia	Cystic Fibrosis	Huntington Disease
Synonym: Sickle cell anaemia	**Synonyms**: Cooley anaemia, Mediterranean anaemia	**Synonyms**: Mucoviscidosis, CF	**Synonyms**: Huntington's chorea, HD (abbreviated)
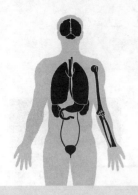	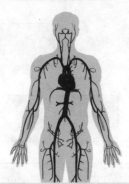	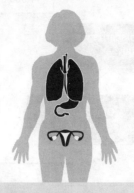	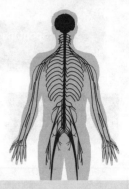
Incidence: Occurs most commonly in people of African ancestry. West Africans: 1% (10-45% carriers) West Indians: 0.5%	**Incidence**: Most common type of thalassaemia affecting 1% of some populations. More common in Asia, Middle East and Mediterranean.	**Incidence**: Varies with populations: United States: 1 in 1,000 (0.1%) Asians in England: 1 in 10,000 Caucasians: 1 in 20-28 are carriers	**Incidence**: An uncommon genetic disease present in 1 in 20 000.
Gene type: Autosomal recessive mutation which results in the substitution of a single nucleotide in the HBB gene that codes for the beta chain of haemoglobin.	**Gene type**: Autosomal recessive mutation of the HBB gene coding for the haemoglobin beta chain. It may arise through a gene deletion or a nucleotide deletion or insertion.	**Gene type**: Autosomal recessive. Over 500 different recessive mutations (deletions, missense, nonsense, terminator codon) of the CFTR gene have been identified.	**Gene type**: An autosomal dominant mutation of the HD gene (IT15) caused by an increase in the length (36-125) of a CAG repeat region (normal range is 11-30 repeats).
Gene location: Chromosome 11 	**Gene location**: Chromosome 11	**Gene location**: Chromosome 7 	**Gene location**: Chromosome 4 
Symptoms: Include: anaemia; mild to severe pain in the chest, joints, back, or abdomen; jaundice; kidney failure; repeated infections, in particular pneumonia or meningitis; eye problems including blindness; swollen hands and feet; gallstones (at an early age); strokes.	**Symptoms**: The result of haemoglobin with few or no beta chains, causes a severe anaemia during the first few years of life. People with this condition are tired and pale because not enough oxygen reaches the cells.	**Symptoms**: Disruption of glands: the *pancreas*, *intestinal glands*, *biliary tree* (biliary cirrhosis), *bronchial glands* (chronic lung infections), and *sweat glands* (high salt content of which becomes depleted in a hot environment). *Infertility* occurs in males/females.	**Symptoms**: Mutant gene forms defective protein: **huntingtin**. Progressive, selective *nerve cell death* associated with chorea (jerky, involuntary movements), *psychiatric disorders*, and *dementia* (memory loss, disorientation, impaired ability to reason, and personality changes).
Treatment and outlook: Patients are given folic acid. Acute episodes may require oxygen therapy, intravenous infusions of fluid, and antibiotic drugs. Experimental therapies include bone marrow transplants and gene therapy.	**Treatment and outlook**: Patients require frequent blood transfusions. This causes iron build-up in the organs, which is treated with drugs. Bone marrow transplants and gene therapy hold promise and are probable future treatments.	**Treatment and outlook**: Conventional: chest physiotherapy, a modified diet, and the use of TOBI antibiotic to control lung infections. Outlook: Gene transfer therapy inserting normal CFTR gene using adenovirus vectors and liposomes.	**Treatment and outlook**: Surgical treatment may be possible. Research is underway to discover drugs that interfere with *huntingtin* protein. Genetic counselling coupled with genetic screening of embryos may be developed in the future.

1. For each of the genetic disorder below, indicate the following:

   (a) Sickle cell disease: Gene name: __HBB__   Chromosome: __11__   Mutation type: _Substitution_

   (b) β-thalassaemia: Gene name: _____   Chromosome: _____   Mutation type: _____

   (c) Cystic fibrosis: Gene name: _____   Chromosome: _____   Mutation type: _____

   (d) Huntington disease: Gene name: _____   Chromosome: _____   Mutation type: _____

2. Explain the cause of the symptoms for people suffering from β-thalassaemia: _____

   _____

3. Suggest a reason for the differences in the country-specific incidence rates for some genetic disorders:

   _____

   _____

Code: A 2

Non-infectious Disease

The Fate of Conceptions

A significant number of conceptions do not end in live births. Even those that do may still have problems. A large proportion of miscarriages, which are spontaneous natural abortions, are caused by **chromosome disorders**: trisomy, polyploidy, and missing pieces of chromosomes. Some chromosome abnormalities are less severe than others and those affected survive into childhood or beyond. There is a strong correlation between the age of the mother and the incidence in chromosome abnormalities, called the **maternal age effect**. Prospective mothers older than 35-40 years of age are therefore encouraged to have a prenatal test (e.g. **amniocentesis** or **CVS**) to establish whether the foetus has a normal chromosome complement.

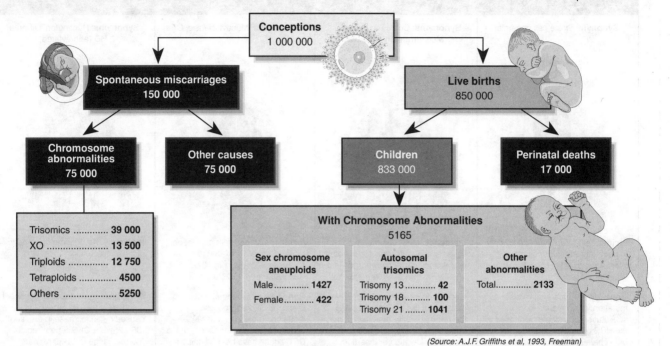

Conceptions
1 000 000

Spontaneous miscarriages
150 000

Live births
850 000

Chromosome abnormalities
75 000

Other causes
75 000

Children
833 000

Perinatal deaths
17 000

Trisomics	39 000
XO	13 500
Triploids	12 750
Tetraploids	4500
Others	5250

With Chromosome Abnormalities
5165

Sex chromosome aneuploids	Autosomal trisomics	Other abnormalities
Male 1427	Trisomy 13 42	Total 2133
Female 422	Trisomy 18 100	
	Trisomy 21 1041	

(Source: A.J.F. Griffiths et al, 1993, Freeman)

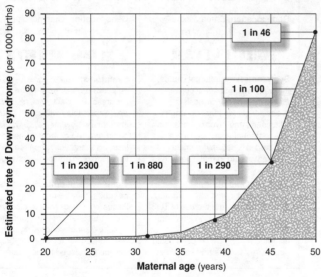

1 in 46
1 in 100
1 in 2300
1 in 880
1 in 290

Estimated rate of Down syndrome (per 1000 births)
Maternal age (years)

Incidence of Down syndrome related to maternal age

Maternal age (years)	Incidence per 1,000 live births
< 30	< 1
30 - 34	1 - 2
35 - 39	2 - 5
40 - 44	5 - 10
> 44	10 - 20

(data for European women)

The table (above) and the graph (left) show different representations of the maternal age effect on the incidence of **Down syndrome**. The older the prospective mother is, the more likely it is that she will have an affected child.

1. Discuss the role of the **maternal age effect** in the incidence rate of Down syndrome and other trisomic syndromes:

_____

_____

_____

2. Explain the role of **amniocentesis** in detecting trisomic disorders: _____

_____

_____

3. Explain why, in recent times, most Down syndrome babies are born to younger mothers: _____

_____

_____

Genetic Disorders

Trisomy is a form of **aneuploidy** where the nucleus of the cells in an organism have one chromosome pair represented by three chromosomes (2N+1). The extra chromosome can grossly disturb the overall chromosomal balance resulting in abnormalities or death. In humans, about 50% of all spontaneous abortions result from chromosomal abnormalities, and trisomies are responsible for about half of these (25% of all spontaneous abortions). About 6% of live births result in children born with chromosomal abnormalities. Autosomal trisomies make up only 0.1% of all pregnancies. Of the three trisomics that survive to birth, **Down** syndrome (see below) is the most common. The other two trisomies, **Edward** and **Patau**, show severe mental and physical abnormalities (see below). Trisomy may be found in a few other autosomes, but they are extremely rare.

Down Syndrome (Trisomy 21)

Down syndrome is the most common of the human aneuploidies. The incidence rate in humans is about 1 in 800 births for women aged 30 to 31 years, with a maternal age effect (the rate increases rapidly with maternal age). The most common form of this condition arises when meiosis fails to separate the pair of chromosome number 21s in the eggs that are forming in the woman's ovaries (it is apparently rare for males to be the cause of this condition). In addition to growth failure and mental retardation, there are a number of well known phenotypic traits (see diagram right).

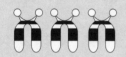

21

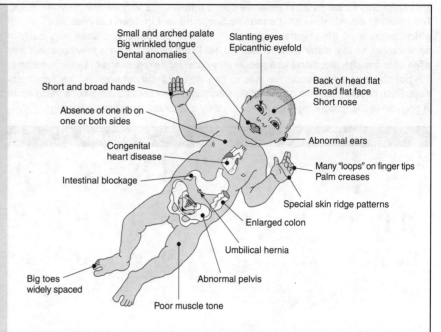

- Small and arched palate
- Big wrinkled tongue
- Dental anomalies
- Slanting eyes
- Epicanthic eyefold
- Short and broad hands
- Back of head flat
- Broad flat face
- Short nose
- Absence of one rib on one or both sides
- Abnormal ears
- Congenital heart disease
- Many "loops" on finger tips
- Palm creases
- Intestinal blockage
- Special skin ridge patterns
- Enlarged colon
- Umbilical hernia
- Big toes widely spaced
- Abnormal pelvis
- Poor muscle tone

Edward Syndrome (Trisomy 18)

Edward syndrome has an incidence rate of 1 in 5000 live births (with a maternal age effect). Features include severe mental retardation, low set, malformed ears, congenital heart defects, small mouth and rocker-bottom feet. Half the patients die by two months of age, and only a few have been known to survive beyond several years of age. About 95% of the affected foetuses are spontaneously aborted.

18

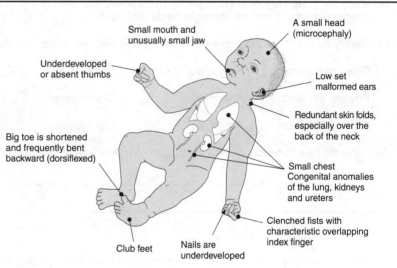

- Small mouth and unusually small jaw
- A small head (microcephaly)
- Underdeveloped or absent thumbs
- Low set malformed ears
- Redundant skin folds, especially over the back of the neck
- Big toe is shortened and frequently bent backward (dorsiflexed)
- Small chest
- Congenital anomalies of the lung, kidneys and ureters
- Clenched fists with characteristic overlapping index finger
- Club feet
- Nails are underdeveloped

Patau Syndrome (Trisomy 13)

Patau syndrome has an incidence rate of 1 in 3000 live births (with a maternal age effect). All patients have markedly retarded mental and physical development, including various eye defects, cleft palate and cleft lip, polydactyly, low set, malformed ears and a variety of defects of internal organs. About half the affected babies die by one month of age with a rare instance of one patient surviving to age 10 years.

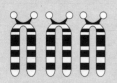

13

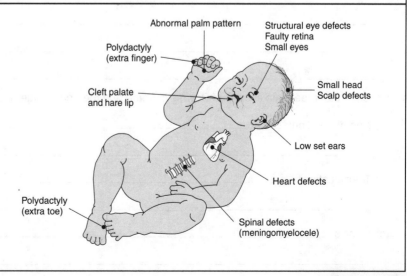

- Abnormal palm pattern
- Structural eye defects
- Faulty retina
- Small eyes
- Polydactyly (extra finger)
- Cleft palate and hare lip
- Small head
- Scalp defects
- Low set ears
- Heart defects
- Polydactyly (extra toe)
- Spinal defects (meningomyelocele)

Non-infectious Disease

Code: A 3

The Causes of Down Syndrome

Sir J. Langdon Down described this syndrome in 1886. Many studies over the past years have lead us to better understanding how trisomy 21 syndrome may arise. There are three different ways in which Down syndrome can arise. Nearly all cases (approximately 95%) result from **non-disjunction** of chromosome 21 during **meiosis**. However, one in twenty cases (fewer than 3-4%) of Down syndrome arises from a **translocation** mutation where the parent is a translocation carrier (chromosome 21 is fused to another chromosome, usually number 14). A small proportion of cases (fewer than 3%) arise from the failure of the pair of chromosomes 21 to separate during **mitosis** at a very early embryonic stage. The resulting individual is called a **mosaic** due to the fact that two cell lines exist, one of which differs from the original zygote. If the mitotic abnormality occurs very early in development, so that many cells are affected, full Down syndrome traits may appear. If only a few cells are affected, then these people may show mild expressions of Down syndrome. It is possible that many people are mosaic for trisomy 21 without showing any significant traits. Such people may have only a small proportion of their cells trisomic, but if these occur in gonadal tissue (producing eggs or sperm) they may produce trisomic offspring.

Karyotype A	Karyotype B	Karyotype C
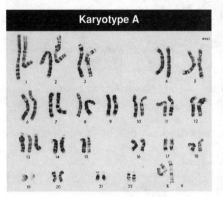	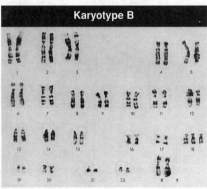	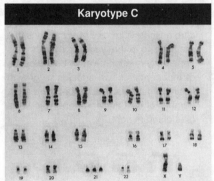

Karyotype photos: Cytogenetics Dept, Waikato Hospital

1. (a) Study the three karyotype photographs (A-C) above and identify the three chromosomes (trisomy) that cause the syndromes listed below by placing a **circle** around them.

   (b) Identify each of the karyotypes (A-C) above, and state which chromosome is trisomic, and its incidence rate:

   Down syndrome: Karyotype: _____ Chromosome: _____ Incidence rate: _____

   Edward syndrome: Karyotype: _____ Chromosome: _____ Incidence rate: _____

   Patau syndrome: Karyotype: _____ Chromosome: _____ Incidence rate: _____

2. Describe the classic features of the phenotype of a Down syndrome person: _____

   _____

   _____

   _____

3. Explain why the presence of an extra chromosome has such a profound effect on the development of phenotype:

   _____

   _____

   _____

   _____

4. Describe the three main causes of Down syndrome and the percentage of cases arising for each:

   (a) Non-disjunction: _____

   _____

   (b) Translocation: _____

   _____

   (c) Mosaic: _____

   _____

Infectious Disease

Investigating the nature of infectious disease: viral, bacterial, and fungal pathogens, parasites, & prions

Modes of transmission and vectors of disease, pathogens and their immunity to disease, case studies in human diseases.

Learning Objectives

☐ 1. Compile your own glossary from the **KEY WORDS** displayed in **bold type** in the learning objectives below.

The Nature of Disease *(pages 28, 51-55, 71-72)*

☐ 2. Define the terms **disease**, **infection**, **symptom**. Distinguish between **infectious disease** and non-infectious disease. Identify the role of **pathogens** in disease and list examples from different taxa.

☐ 3. Distinguish between a **pandemic** and an **epidemic**, and between **aetiology** and **epidemiology**. Identify the sort of information provided by epidemiological studies.

☐ 4. Recognise the contributions of **Robert Koch** and **Louis Pasteur** to the identification of microorganisms as the agents of disease. Outline **Koch's postulates** and explain how Koch's methodology helped to clarify the association between pathogens and disease.

☐ 5. Explain the modes of **transmission** for infectious diseases in populations. Explain the role of hygiene and sanitation in controlling some infectious diseases.

☐ 6. Distinguish between pathogens and **parasites** and between **endoparasites** and **ectoparasites**. Appreciate that some parasites can be **vectors** of disease, even if they do not cause it directly.

☐ 7. With respect to parasites, explain the terms: **primary host**, **secondary** (or intermediate) **host**. Using a named example, explain how parasitic stages are transmitted from host to host. Describe some of the adaptations of parasites that enable them to successfully locate a suitable host.

☐ 8. Describe the cause, transmission, effects (including host response and symptoms), prevention, treatment, and control of at least one named infectious disease. You could choose from the case studies provided, or use an example of a locally occurring disease.

Viral Diseases *(pages 56-58, 91-93, 97)*

☐ 9. Identify the structural and functional features of **viruses** that make them such host-specific pathogens. Identify the genetic and morphological features important in distinguishing different viral types. Using a named example, describe how viral diseases are transmitted and how they infect a host and cause disease.

☐ 10. Explain the features of modern-day society that make widespread epidemics of virulent diseases more likely. Providing examples, explain the role of **vaccination** in the past and present control of viral diseases. Explain why it is difficult to develop vaccines against, or cures for, some viral diseases (e.g. HIV).

Case study: HIV/AIDS *(pages 59-62)*

☐ 11. Discuss the cause, transmission, and social implications of **HIV/AIDS**. Include reference to the role of social, economic, and biological factors in the distribution, spread, treatment, and control of AIDS.

☐ 12. Identify stages in the development of an HIV infection, including the effect of HIV on the immune system. Explain why AIDS is termed a **syndrome**.

☐ 13. Describe the probable origins of the two strains of HIV as cross species transfers (**zoonoses**).

Bacterial Disease *(pages 63-64, 91-93, 97)*

☐ 14. Identify the ways in which pathogenic bacteria cause disease. Giving examples, identify how bacterial diseases are transmitted. Relate the type and incidence of bacterial disease to the prevailing social conditions.

☐ 15. Describe factors affecting bacterial **pathogenicity**, including: features of the cell wall and capsule, **toxin** production, **infectivity**, and **invasiveness**. Distinguish between **exotoxins** (e.g *Staphylococcus*) and **endotoxins** (e.g. *Salmonella*). Recognise **enterotoxins** as exotoxins that affect the gastrointestinal tract.

☐ 16. With reference to **disinfectants**, **antiseptics**, and **antibiotics**, describe how bacterial diseases are controlled and treated.

Case study: tuberculosis (TB) *(page 65)*

☐ 17. Describe the causes and modes of transmission of TB. Assess the global importance of TB and understand its history in the human population, including reference to its **prevalence**, decline, and **reemergence**. Explain the importance of **carriers** in the spread of TB.

☐ 18. Discuss the treatment of TB, including the difficulties associated with increasing bacterial resistance to antibiotics. Describe the roles of social, economic, and biological factors in the control and prevention of TB.

Contamination of food and water *(pages 66, 91)*

☐ 19. Appreciate the role of inadequate provision of clean drinking water, poor sanitation, and/or poor food hygiene in the transmission of food and water-borne pathogens. Provide examples of food and waterborne diseases spread by the **faecal-oral route**.

Case study: food poisoning

☐ 20. Describe the causes and modes of transmission of **salmonellosis** and/or **staphylococcal food poisoning**. Describe factors governing the occurrence, prevention, and severity of these diseases.

Case study: cholera *(pages 67, 91)*

☐ 21. Describe the agent involved and modes of transmission of **cholera**. Assess the past and current global importance of cholera and relate its distribution to factors such as levels of sanitation and general poverty.

22. Discuss the roles of social, economic, and biological factors in controlling, preventing, and treating cholera.

Fungal Diseases *(pages 68, 93)*

23. Only a few fungi are pathogenic to humans and most of the diseases they cause tend to be **superficial diseases** of the skin and nails. Describe some of the fungal diseases affecting humans and identify the pathogen in each case.

24. Describe how fungi reproduce and infect a host and appreciate why many fungal diseases tend to be **chronic** infections. Describe how **fungicides** are used in the treatment of fungal diseases.

Protozoan Diseases *(pages 69-70, 91-92)*

25. Describe the nature of **protozoa** (amoebae, ciliates, sporozoans, and flagellates). Explain how some pathogenic **protozoans** are also parasites with part of their life cycle occurring within a human.

Case study: malaria

26. Identify the pathogen and mode of transmission of **malaria**. Assess malaria's global importance and identify biological factors in its distribution.

27. Describe the roles of social, economic, and biological factors in treating, controlling, and preventing malaria. Comment on the adequacy of these methods with reference to the difficulties associated with developing drugs against protozoans.

Multicellular Parasites *(pages 71-74)*

28. Describe the disease caused by one of the following multicellular organisms. Include reference to the/ parasite and its mode of transmission and life cycle:
   - Flatworms, e.g. **hydatid tapeworm**, *Schistosoma*.
   - Roundworms, e.g. *Ascaris*, hookworm, and the nematodes that cause trichinosis and elephantiasis.

29. Describe an example of an insect-carried infection of humans. Name some **ectoparasites** and the conditions or diseases for which they are responsible.

Emerging Diseases *(pages 75-78)*

30. Explain what is meant by an **emerging disease** and list some examples. Identify the threat that emerging diseases present to public health. Explain how emerging diseases may arise (e.g. through cross species transfer as a **zoonosis**) and cite examples.

31. Describe the nature of **prion diseases** and identify examples. Describe their mode of transmission, how they are thought to causes disease, the time period for development of symptoms, and the mortality.

32. Describe the agent involved and modes of transmission of a named emerging disease (other than HIV/AIDS). Identify the factors governing its emergence, global spread, and **virulence**, and explain how the pathogen was isolated and identified. Examples could include vCJD, Legionnaires' disease, SARS, or avian flu.

See page 7 for additional details of these texts:

- Chenn, P. 1997. **Microorganisms and Biotechnology** (John Murray), Chpt 9 as required.
- Clegg, C.J., 2002. **Microbes in Action**, (John Murray), chpt 1-5, 10 (treatment covered in context).
- Freeland, P., 1999. **Microbes, Medicine and Commerce** (Hodder & Stoughton), chpt 2.
- Fullick, A., 2000. **Human Health and Disease** (Heinemann), chpt 2.
- Hudson, T. & K. Mannion, 2001. **Microbes and Disease** (Collins), chpt 4 and 5.
- Murray, P. & N. Owens, 2001. **Behaviour and Populations** (Collins), chpt 6 and 7.
- Taylor, J., 2001. **Microorganisms and Biotechnology** (NelsonThornes), chpt 8.

See page 7 for details of publishers of periodicals:

STUDENT'S REFERENCE

- **War on Disease** National Geographic 201(2) February 2002, pp. 4-31. *A great overview of the global importance of a range of infectious diseases.*
- **Koch's Postulates** Biol. Sci. Rev., 15(3) February 2003, pp. 24-25. *Koch's postulates and the diagnosis of infectious disease.*
- **Viral Plagues** Biol. Sci. Rev., 17(3) February 2005, pp. 37-41. *The nature of viruses and viral diseases, and what we can do to combat them.*
- **The White Plague** New Scientist (Inside Science), 9 Nov. 2002. *The causes and nature of TB, an update on the global incidence of this disease, and a discussion of the implications of increasing drug resistance to TB treatment.*
- **Tuberculosis** Biol. Sci. Rev., 14(1) Sept. 2001, pp. 30-33. *Despite vaccination, TB has become more common recently. Why has it returned?*

- **Malaria** Biol. Sci. Rev., 15(1) Sept. 2002, pp. 29-33. *An account of the world's most important parasitic infection of humans. Symptoms, control and prevention, and future treatment options, as well as the parasite's life cycle, are discussed.*
- **Beating the Bloodsuckers** Biol. Sci. Rev., 16(3) Feb. 2004, pp. 31-35. *The nature and extent of malaria, including the biology of the Plasmodium parasite and the body's immune response to it.*
- **Food / How Safe?** National Geographic, May 2002, pp. 2-31. *An excellent account of the issue of food safety and bacterial contamination of food.*
- *Campylobacter jejuni* Biol. Sci. Rev., 15(1) Sept. 2002, pp. 26-28. *An account of the diseases caused by Campylobacter, an increasingly common contaminant of food. Preventative measures are also discussed.*
- **Salmonella** Biol. Sci. Rev., 10(4) March 1998, pp.6-8. *Salmonella is an infectious bacterium which causes food poisoning and is a common contaminant of poultry and packaged foods.*
- **No Mercy** New Scientist, 14 October 2000, pp. 28-32. *The flu virus: transmission and the spread of pandemics. This article also examines the role of animals as reservoirs for new flu strains.*
- **Bacteria Can Count!** Biol. Sci. Rev., 13(2) November 2000, pp. 28-31. *The nature of bacteria and how they invade tissues and create infection.*
- **Food / How Safe?** National Geographic, May 2002, pp. 2-31. *An excellent account of the issue of food safety and bacterial contamination of food.*
- **Escherichia coli O157** Biol. Sci. Rev., 10(3) Jan. 1998, pp. 9-11. *Transmission of disease by this virulent strain of E. coli. Covers symptoms, spread and control of the disease.*
- **A Worm's Life** Biol. Sci. Rev.,13(5) May 2001, pp. 20-23. *Multicellular parasitic diseases and the threat they pose to human health (includes morphology and life cycle of a nematode worm).*
- **Schistosomiasis** Biol. Sci. Rev., 16(3) Feb. 2004, pp. 21-25. *An account of the life cycle and reproductive biology of the schistosome fluke.*
- **Fungi: Friends or Foes** Biol. Sci. Rev., 17(1) Sept. 2004, pp. 24-28. *The nature of fungi, including their contributions in medicine and their role as pathogens. Mycotoxins and the treatment of fungal diseases are also covered.*
- **Positive Progress** New Scientist, 8 Feb. 2003, pp. 33-45. *A series of articles focusing on current issues in HIV research: why some individuals*

do not contract AIDS, the latest in vaccine development, and new measures against infection.
- **Search for a Cure** National Geographic 201(2) February 2002, pp. 32-43. *A current account of the global status of the AIDS epidemic, and an examination of the measures to stop it.*
- **Opportunistic Infections and AIDS** Biol. Sci. Rev., 14 (4) April 2002, pp. 21-24. *An account of the suite of infections characterising AIDS (good).*
- **Living with AIDS** National Geographic 208(3) Sept. 2005, pp. 66-73. *South Africans share their experiences of living with AIDS. This account includes a world map in which each country's size reflects the number of people with HIV/AIDS.*
- **Tracking the Next Flu Killer** National Geographic 208(4) Oct. 2005, pp. 4-31. *Avian flu compared with the 1918 Spanish flu and predictions of a possible bird flu pandemic.*

See pages 4-5 for details of how to access **Bio Links** from our web site: **www.thebiozone.com** From Bio Links, access sites under the topics:

HEALTH & DISEASE: • CDC disease links • CDC: Avian influenza • WHO/OMS: health topics > **Infectious Diseases:** • Centers for Disease Control and Prevention (CDC) • Cholera and epidemic dysentery • Disease-causing bacteria • Emerging infectious diseases • HIV Insite: gateway to AIDS knowledge • Koch's postulates • Meningococcal disease • Prion diseases • Public Health Laboratory Service: Disease facts • The bad bug book • The science of HIV Insect vectors of human pathogens • SARS (from WHO) • Coronaviruses • SARS quarantine... *and others*

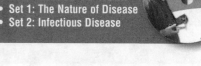

Presentation MEDIA to support this topic:

Health & Disease CD-ROM:
- Set 1: The Nature of Disease
- Set 2: Infectious Disease

Infection and Disease

The term disease often refers to **infectious disease**; disease caused by an infectious agent or **pathogen**. In 1861, **Louis Pasteur** demonstrated experimentally that microorganisms can be present in non-living matter and can contaminate seemingly sterile solutions. He also showed conclusively that microbes can be destroyed by heat; a discovery that formed the basis of modern-day **aseptic technique**. The development of the germ theory of disease followed Pasteur's discoveries and, in 1876-1877, **Robert Koch** established a sequence of experimental steps (now known as **Koch's postulates**) for directly relating a specific microbe to a specific disease. During the past 100 years, the postulates have been invaluable in determining the specific agents of many diseases.

Infectious Disease

Pathogens and Parasites

Pathogens are organisms that cause disease. Some pathogens are also (intra- or extracellular) parasites and seek to exploit the rich food resources of the host and use the host's tissues as incubators for their own reproduction. The invasion of the body by pathogens is called **infection**. Pathogens can be classified as microorganisms (bacteria, fungi, and viruses) or macroorganisms (i.e. organisms visible to the naked eye, such as worms, ticks, and mites). Macroorganisms can cause disease as a direct result of their activity, or they can serve as **vectors** for the transmission of other infectious agents.

Robert Koch

In 1876-1877, the German physician Robert Koch demonstrated that a specific infectious disease (anthrax) was caused by a specific microorganism (*Bacillus anthracis*). From his work he devised what are now known as **Koch's postulates**.

Koch's postulates

1. The same pathogen must be present in every case of the disease.
2. The pathogen must be isolated from the diseased host and grown in pure culture.
3. The pathogen from the pure culture must cause the disease when it is introduced by inoculation into a healthy, but susceptible organism (usually animal).
4. The pathogen must be isolated from the inoculated animal and be shown to be the original organism.

Exceptions to Koch's Postulates

- Some bacteria and viruses cannot be grown on artificial media (they multiply only within cells).
- Some pathogens cause several disease conditions (e.g. *Mycobacterium tuberculosis*, *Streptococcus pyogenes*).

Types of Pathogens

Bacteria: All bacteria are prokaryotes, but they are diverse in both their structure and metabolism. Bacteria are categorised according to the properties of their cell walls and characteristics such as cell shape and arrangements, oxygen requirement, and motility. Many bacteria are useful, but the relatively few species that are pathogenic are responsible for enormous social and economic cost.

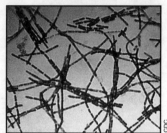

Bacillus anthracis: the rod-shaped bacterial pathogen that causes anthrax

Eukaryotic pathogens: Eukaryotic pathogens (fungi, algae, protozoa, and parasitic worms) include the pathogens responsible for malaria and schistosomiasis. Many are highly specialised parasites with a number of hosts. Serious fungal diseases are also more prevalent now than in the past, affecting those with compromised immune systems, such as AIDS patients.

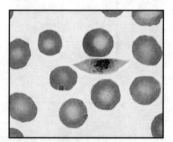

The malarial parasite, *Plasmodium*, seen in a red blood cell smear.

Viral pathogens: Viruses are responsible for many of the everyday diseases with which we are familiar (e.g. the common cold), as well as rather more alarming and dangerous diseases, such as Ebola. Viruses were first distinguished from other pathogens because of their small size and because they are obligate intracellular parasites and need living host cells in order to multiply.

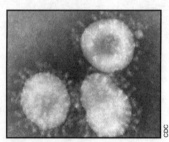

The *Coronavirus* responsible for the 2003 global epidemic of SARS.

1. Using a named example, explain what is meant by a **pathogen**: _____

_____

2. Explain the contribution of Robert Koch to the **aetiology** of disease: _____

_____

_____

3. Suggest why diseases caused by **intracellular protozoan parasites** can be particularly difficult to control and treat:

_____

_____

The Role of Health Statistics

Health is difficult to define and to measure, and most of the information about the state of health of a nation's population comes from studying disease. **Epidemiology** is the study of the occurrence and the spread of disease. The **health statistics** collected by epidemiologists are used by health authorities to identify patterns of disease in their country. These patterns, including the **incidence** and **prevalence** of a disease are important in planning health services and investigating causes of disease. Health statistics enable the effectiveness of health policies and practices, such as vaccination programmes, to be monitored. The World Health Organisation (WHO) gathers data on an international basis to identify global patterns.

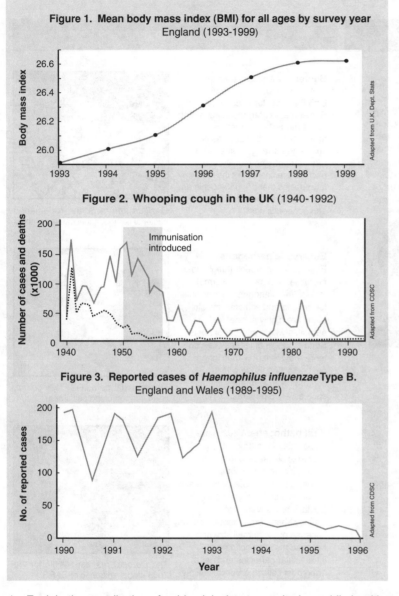

Figure 1. Mean body mass index (BMI) for all ages by survey year
England (1993-1999)

Adapted from U.K. Dept. Stats

Figure 2. Whooping cough in the UK (1940-1992)

Immunisation introduced

Adapted from CDSC

Figure 3. Reported cases of *Haemophilus influenzae* Type B.
England and Wales (1989-1995)

Adapted from CDSC

The causes of illness and death for people in developing countries are very different from those in affluent societies.

Figure 4. The causes of death in developed and developing countries, 1998

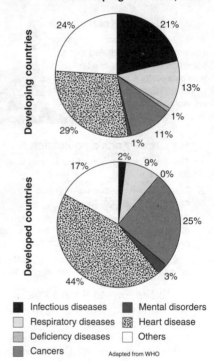

Developing countries

24%   21%
      13%
      1%
29%   11%
   1%

Developed countries

      2%   9%
17%   0%
           25%
44%   3%

■ Infectious diseases   ■ Mental disorders
□ Respiratory diseases ▨ Heart disease
■ Deficiency diseases   □ Others
■ Cancers   Adapted from WHO

1. Explain the contribution of epidemiologists to monitoring public health: _____

_____

2. Describe the trend in BMI between 1993 and 1999 (Figure 1): _____

_____

3. (a) Suggest a probable reason for the pattern of reported cases of *Haemophilus influenzae* (Figure 3) prior to 1993:

_____

   (b) Suggest a possible cause for the decline in the incidence of *Haemophilius influenzae* after 1993: _____

_____

4. (a) Identify a difference between the cause of death between developed and developing countries: _____

_____

   (b) Suggest a reason for this difference: _____

Patterns of Disease

Diseases present in low levels of a population at any time are known as **endemic** diseases. Occasionally there may be a sudden increase in the **prevalence** of a particular disease. On a local level this is known as an **outbreak**. Such an increase in prevalence on a national scale is called an **epidemic**. An epidemic occurs when an infectious disease spreads rapidly through a population and affects large numbers of people. One example is influenza, epidemics of which are relatively common and occur every two to three years. On rare occasions an epidemic disease will spread to other countries throughout the world. This is known as a **pandemic**. Examples

of diseases that are known to have caused pandemics are bubonic plague, cholera, tuberculosis, HIV/AIDS, and influenza. **Epidemiologists** gather data on the number of infected people (**morbidity**) and the number of people that have died (**mortality**) within a population. These data help to establish the **incidence** (number of new cases per unit time) and **prevalence** (number of infected people expressed as a proportion of the population) of the disease in the population at any given time. **Aetiology** is the study of the cause of a disease. It can assist in pinpointing the origin of new diseases, such as the respiratory disease SARS, as they arise in populations.

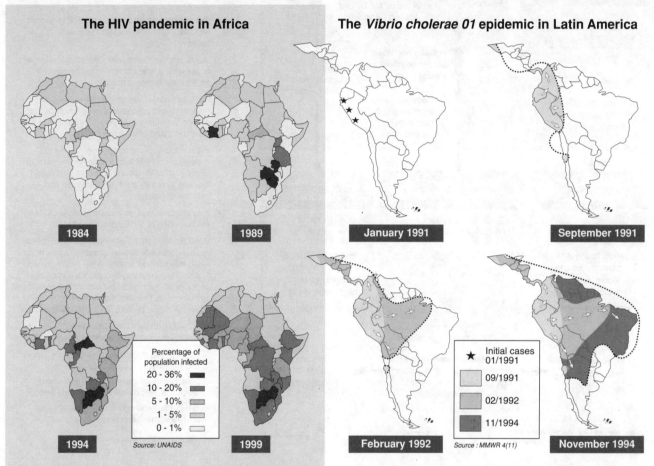

The HIV pandemic in Africa

1984 · 1989

Percentage of population infected
20 - 36%
10 - 20%
5 - 10%
1 - 5%
0 - 1%

1994 · *Source: UNAIDS* · 1999

The *Vibrio cholerae 01* epidemic in Latin America

January 1991 · September 1991

★ Initial cases 01/1991
09/1991
02/1992
11/1994

February 1992 · *Source : MMWR 4(11)* · November 1994

The figure above shows the spread of HIV through Africa as part of the current global pandemic. More than 36 million people are infected with HIV worldwide and 70% of those infected live in sub-Saharan Africa. In this region, seven countries have an adult prevalence of 20% or higher, including Botswana where 36% of the population is infected.

Cholera had not been reported in Latin America for over a century before the initial outbreaks occurred in January, 1991. Cholera is transmitted through ingestion of food and beverages contaminated with faeces, or by bathing in faecally contaminated water. By the time the epidemic began to subside in 1994, more than 1 million cases and nearly 10 000 deaths had been reported. Death rates were high as a result of inadequate provision for oral rehydration.

1. Using examples, distinguish between different patterns of disease (epidemic, pandemic, and endemic disease):

_____

_____

_____

_____

_____

2. Suggest why it is important to establish the **incidence** of a disease when it begins to spread through a community:

_____

_____

Code: A 2

The Initial Spread of SARS in Toronto, Canada
(February – April, 2003)

Kwan Sui-Chu travels to Hong Kong in February, contracts **Severe Acute Respiratory Syndrome** (SARS) at the Metropole Hotel from a "super spreader", and returns home to Toronto where she infects her family. She later dies of SARS on March 5.

Kwan's Family

Tse Chi Kwai (son) → Wife of **Tse's** doctor

The Containment of an Epidemic

The global SARS outbreak in 2003 developed quickly and dramatically. Its containment required heroic efforts and extraordinary measures. Health systems at every major outbreak site were strained to the limits of their capacity. The last reported case of SARS from this initial epidemic was detected and isolated, in Taiwan, on 15 June 2003.

Health authorities rapidly introduced a series of sweeping measures, including:

- Vigorous tracing of every possible contact with a SARS patient.

- Immediate quarantine of individuals suspected (but not confirmed) of having SARS (enforced with the threat of execution in the case of mainland China).

- Surveillance systems were upgraded and began to deliver the kind of information needed for prompt and targeted action.

- Hospital procedures for infection control were tightened, and procedures were developed to ensure the efficient delivery of protective equipment and other supplies.

- Mass education campaigns persuaded the population to check frequently for fever and report promptly at fever clinics. This greatly reduced the time between onset of symptoms and isolation of patients.

- A mechanism was established for coordinating the response of all relevant agencies.

- WHO issued rare travel advisories as evidence mounted that SARS was spreading by air travel along international routes. WHO recommended that persons traveling to certain regions/cities consider postponing all but essential travel until further notice. This was the most stringent travel advisory issued by WHO in its 55-year history.

- WHO set up three networks of leading laboratories around the world to investigate:

  - speeding up detection of the causative agent and developing a diagnostic test;

  - pooling clinical knowledge on symptoms, diagnosis, and management (treatment);

  - SARS epidemiology (how the disease is spread through a population).

Scarborough Grace Hospital

Joseph Pollack

Tse shares a room with other patients, infecting two of them: "**Mr. D.**" and **Joseph Pollack**

"**Mr. D.**"

In addition, at least 14 hospital staff develop symptoms

Pollack's wife, **Rose**, is infected while in waiting room

"**Mr. D.**" is transferred to York Central

Rose sits next to a prayer group **patriarch** and his **two sons**

Mount Sinai Hospital

A patient had visited a Scarborough clinic; four on Mount Sinai staff develop symptoms

Filipino Prayer Group
(Bukas Loob Sa Diyos)

York Central Hospital

Health officials say "**Mr. D.**" could have exposed dozens. Two other patients die at York

One son travels to a Montreal conference

Patriarch's sons attend father's funeral and two other group functions. At least 30 members are infected.

One son travels to Pennsylvania

Source: *"How One Case Spawned Dozens More"*, TIME Magazine, May 5, 2003, page 36-37.

KEY: Infected   Known dead

Source: World Health Organisation (WHO)

3. Severe Acute Respiratory Disease (SARS) is a serious respiratory disease, which appeared in the human population in 2003 and spread rapidly through coughing and sneezing. Its epidemiology provides a good example of how health authorities can work together to locate the origin of a disease and halt its spread:

(a) Describe the pattern of spread of SARS in Toronto, Canada: _____

_____

(b) Describe the particular features of disease control that were important in containing the spread of SARS:

_____

_____

(c) Identify which aspect of modern life contributed to the rapid global spread of SARS: _____

_____

_____

4. Suggest why aetiology is important when controlling an outbreak of a new disease: _____

_____

Transmission of Disease

The human body is no different to that of other large animals in that it is under constant attack by a wide range of organisms wanting to penetrate its defences. Once inside us, these organisms will seek to reproduce and exploit us for food. Some of these organisms may be pathogens. Pathogens may be transferred from one individual to another by a number of methods (below). The transmission of infectious diseases can be virtually eliminated by observing appropriate personal hygiene procedures, providing adequate sanitation, and chlorinating drinking water.

Portals of Entry

Respiratory tract

The mouth and nose are major entry points for pathogens, particularly airborne viruses, which are inhaled from other people's expelled mucus.

Examples: diphtheria, meningococcal meningitis, tuberculosis, whooping cough, influenza, measles, German measles (rubella), chickenpox.

Gastrointestinal tract

The mouth is one of the few openings where we deliberately place foreign substances into our body. Food is often contaminated with microorganisms, but most of these are destroyed in the stomach.

Examples: cholera, typhoid fever, mumps, hepatitis A, poliomyelitis, bacillary dysentery, salmonellosis.

Urinogenital openings

The urinogenital openings provide entry points for the pathogens responsible for sexually transmitted infections (STIs) and other opportunistic infections (i.e. thrush).

Examples: gonorrhoea, syphilis, HIV, and *E. coli* (a cause of urinary tract infections).

Breaking the skin surface

The skin provides an effective barrier to the entry of most pathogens. However, a cut or abrasion will allow easy entry for pathogens. Some parasites and pathogens have adaptive features that allow them to penetrate the skin surface.

Examples: tetanus, gas gangrene, bubonic plague, hepatitis B, rabies, malaria, leptospirosis, and HIV.

The Body Under Assault

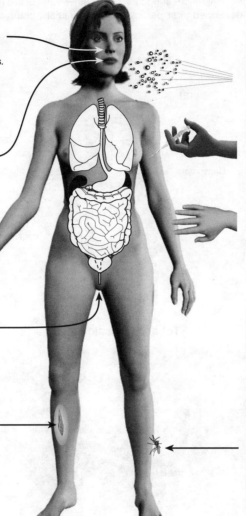

Modes of Transmission

Contact transmission

The agent of disease may occur by contact with other infected humans or animals:

Droplet transmission: Mucus droplets are discharged into the air by coughing, sneezing, laughing, or talking within a radius of 1 m.

Indirect contact: Includes touching objects that have been in contact with the source of infection. Examples include: eating utensils, drinking cups, bedding, toys, money, and used syringes.

Direct contact: Direct transmission of an agent by physical contact between its source and a potential host. Includes touching, kissing, and sexual intercourse. May be person to person, or between humans and other animals.

Vehicle transmission

Agents of disease may be transmitted by a medium such as food, blood, water, intravenous fluids (e.g. drugs), and air. Airborne transmission refers to the spread of fungal spores, some viruses, and bacteria that are transported on dust particles.

Animal Vectors

Some pathogens are transmitted between hosts by other animals. Bites from arthropods (e.g. mosquitoes, ticks, fleas, and lice) and mammals (e.g. rodents) may introduce pathogens, while flies can carry pathogens on their feet. In 1897, **Ronald Ross** identified the *Anopheles* mosquito as the vector for malaria. He was the first to implicate insects in the transmission of disease.

Infectious Disease

1. Describe three personal hygiene practices that would minimise the risk of transmitting an infectious disease:

   (a) _____

   (b) _____

   (c) _____

2. Identify the common **mode of transmission** and the **portal of entry** for the following pathogens:

   (a) Protozoan causing malaria: _____

   (b) Tetanus bacteria: _____

   (c) Cholera bacteria: _____

   (d) Common cold virus: _____

   (e) Tuberculosis bacteria: _____

   (f) HIV (AIDS) virus: _____

   (g) Gonorrhoea bacteria: _____

Code: RA 2

The Structure of Viruses

Viruses are non-cellular **obligate intracellular parasites**, requiring a living host cell in order to reproduce. The traditional view of viruses is as a minimal particle, containing just enough genetic information to infect a host and highjack the host's machinery into replicating more viral particles. The identification in 2004 of a new family of viruses, called mimiviruses, is forcing a rethink of this conservative view. Mimiviruses overlap with parasitic cellular organisms in terms of both size (400 nm) and genome complexity (over 1000 genes) and their existence suggests a fourth domain of life. A typical, fully developed viral particle

(**virion**) lacks the metabolic machinery of cells, containing just a single type of nucleic acid (DNA or RNA) encased in a protein coat or **capsid**. Being non-cellular, they do not conform to the existing criteria upon which a five or six kingdom classification system is based. Viruses can be distinguished by their structure (see below) and by the nature of their genetic material (single or double stranded DNA or RNA). Those that use bacterial cells as a host (**bacteriophages**) can be grown on bacterial cultures, but other viruses are more difficult to study because they require living animals, embryos, or cell cultures in order to replicate.

Viral Structure

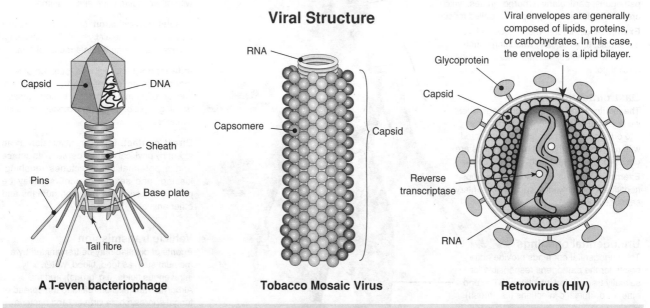

A T-even bacteriophage — Capsid, DNA, Sheath, Pins, Base plate, Tail fibre

Tobacco Mosaic Virus — RNA, Capsomere, Capsid

Retrovirus (HIV) — Viral envelopes are generally composed of lipids, proteins, or carbohydrates. In this case, the envelope is a lipid bilayer. Glycoprotein, Capsid, Reverse transcriptase, RNA

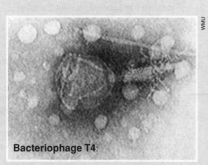

Bacteriophage T4: Some viruses, particularly bacterial viruses (**bacteriophages**) are **complex viruses**, with complicated structures and capsids to which additional structures are attached.

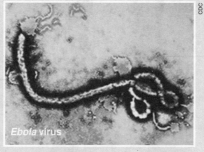

Ebola virus is a filovirus; a group of filament-like, enveloped, helical RNA viruses. Ebola causes a severe, lethal haemorrhagic disease. Outbreaks occur sporadically in Africa.

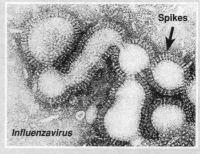

Influenzavirus — Spikes. In some viruses, the capsid is covered by an **envelope**, which protects the virus from the host's nuclease enzymes. *Influenzavirus* is an enveloped virus with many glycoprotein spikes.

1. Describe the basic structure of a generalised virus particle (virion): _____

_____

_____

2. Describe the basis for viral identification: _____

_____

_____

3. Describe the features of viruses that equip them for their role as obligate, intracellular parasites:

_____

_____

_____

Viral Diseases

Viruses are found as parasites in all kinds of organisms including humans and other animals, plants, fungi, bacteria, and protists (protoctists). Some crop and livestock diseases, and many diseases of humans are caused by viruses. Antiviral drugs are difficult to design because they must kill the virus without killing the host cells. Moreover, viruses cannot be attacked when in an inert state. Antiviral drugs work by preventing entry of the virus into the host cell or by interfering with their replication. There are only a few antiviral drugs currently in use (e.g. ribavirin to combat influenza, acyclovir to combat herpes, AZT and protease inhibitors to combat HIV/AIDS). Immunisation is still regarded as the most effective way in which to control viral disease. However immunisation against viruses does not necessarily provide lifelong immunity. New strains of viruses develop as preexisting strains acquire mutations. These mutations allow the viruses to change their surface proteins and thus evade immediate immune system detection.

Human Viral Pathogens

HIV (*Lentivirus*)

The human immunodeficiency virus (HIV) causes AIDS. AIDS is a complex assortment of secondary infections that result after HIV has severely weakened the body's immune system.

Hepatitis viruses

The viruses responsible for hepatitis A, B, and C are not related and are from different viral families. Symptoms include liver damage.

Papillomavirus

This virus causes the formation of warts in humans. Some strains may also transform cells and have been implicated in causing cervical cancer. Host cells may reproduce rapidly, resulting in a tumour.

Herpesviruses

Nearly 100 herpesviruses are known. Types found in humans include those that cause cold sores, chickenpox, shingles, infectious mononucleosis, and genital herpes. They have also been linked to a type of human cancer called Burkitt's lymphoma.

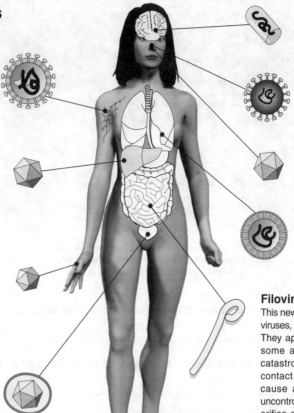

Lyssavirus

This bullet-shaped virus causes rabies and is usually contracted from a bite by a rabid dog or fox.

Coronaviruses

Associated with upper respiratory infections and responsible for 15-20% of colds. A coronavirus is responsible for the disease SARS.

Rhinoviruses

More than 100 rhinoviruses exist and are the most common cause of colds.

Influenzavirus

This virus causes influenza (the flu) in humans. The ability of this virus to rapidly mutate results in many strains.

Filoviruses

This newly emerged group of viruses, called thread-viruses, includes the dangerous Marburg and Ebola. They appear to have recently made a shift from some animal into the human population with catastrophic results. Filoviruses are spread by contact with contaminated blood or tissue and cause a severe form of haemorrhagic fever; uncontrolled bleeding occurs from just about every orifice of the body. Eventually, all internal body organs are affected by massive internal bleeding, causing death.

1. **Complete** the following table summarising the features of selected viral diseases. Use the illustration above to assist you (for disease symptoms, consult a textbook, a good dictionary or an encyclopedia):

Virus	Natural reservoir	Diseases caused	Symptoms
(a) HIV	Infected humans	Acquired Immune Deficiency Syndrome (AIDS)	Exhausted immune system results in cancers and a wide range of opportunistic infections by bacteria, viruses, fungi, and protozoa
(b) Hepatitis viruses			
(c) Coronaviruses		Colds and upper respiratory infections. SARS.	
(d) Rhinoviruses			
(e) *Influenzavirus*			
(f) Filoviruses	Unknown		

Infectious Disease

How Viruses Cause Disease

After entering a host cell, viruses can cause disease in the body by:
■ Invading, destroying, or disrupting the activities of the host cells.
■ Triggering the immune response leading to disease or symptoms of infection, e.g. fever.
■ Interacting with the host's chromosomes to cause cancer (e.g. cervical cancer is linked to human papillomavirus infection).
■ Disrupting the cell-mediated response of the immune system (e.g. HIV destroys T cells and weakens the immune system).

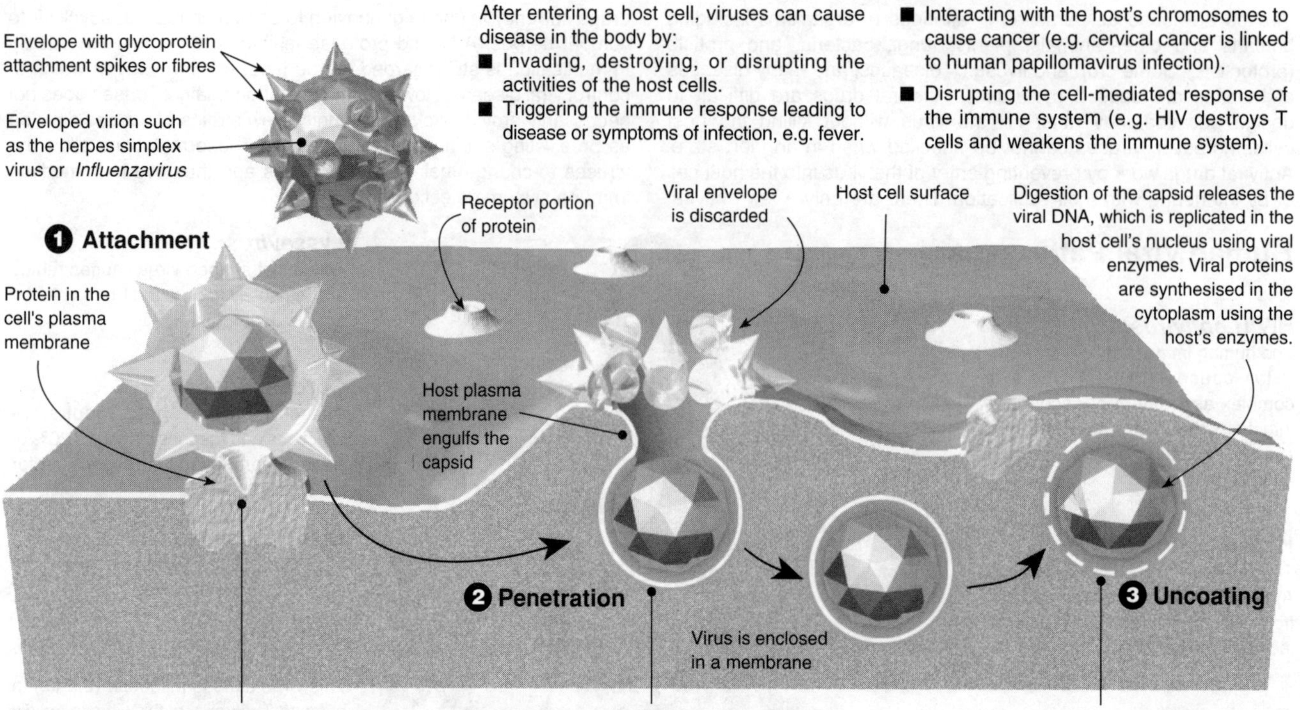

Envelope with glycoprotein attachment spikes or fibres

Enveloped virion such as the herpes simplex virus or *Influenzavirus*

❶ Attachment

Protein in the cell's plasma membrane

Receptor portion of protein

Viral envelope is discarded

Host cell surface

Digestion of the capsid releases the viral DNA, which is replicated in the host cell's nucleus using viral enzymes. Viral proteins are synthesised in the cytoplasm using the host's enzymes.

Host plasma membrane engulfs the capsid

❷ Penetration

Virus is enclosed in a membrane

❸ Uncoating

When a viral particle encounters the outer surface of a body cell, it attaches to the receptor sites of proteins on the cell's plasma membrane.

Once the viral particle is attached, the host cell begins to engulf the virus by **endocytosis**. This is the cell's usual response to foreign particles.

The nucleic acid core is uncoated and the synthesis of new viral particles begins. After maturing, these are released to infect other cells.

2. State the purpose of the glycoprotein spikes found on some enveloped viruses: _____

_____

3. (a) Explain the significance of endocytosis to the entry of an enveloped virus into an animal cell: _____

_____

(b) State where an enveloped virus replicates its viral DNA: _____

(c) State where an enveloped virus synthesises its proteins: _____

4. Summarise the steps involved in invasion of a host cell by an enveloped viral particle such as *Influenzavirus*:

(a) Attachment: _____

_____

(b) Penetration: _____

_____

(c) Uncoating: _____

_____

5. Giving an example, explain why it is difficult to develop suitable long term vaccines against some viruses: _____

_____

_____

6. Explain how viruses may cause some forms of cancer: _____

_____

7. Identify two ways in which viruses can cause disease:

(a) _____

(b) _____

HIV and AIDS

AIDS (acquired immune deficiency syndrome) first appeared in the news in 1981, with cases being reported in Los Angeles, in the United States. By 1983, the pathogen causing the disease had been identified as a retrovirus that selectively infects **helper T cells**. The disease causes a massive deficiency in the immune system due to infection with **HIV** (human immunodeficiency virus). HIV is a retrovirus (RNA, not DNA) and is able to splice its genes into the host cell's chromosome. As yet, there is no cure or vaccine, and the disease has taken the form of a **pandemic**, spreading to all parts of the globe and killing more than a million people each year. It has now been established that HIV arose by the recombination of two simian viruses. It has probably been endemic in some central African regions for decades, as HIV has been found in blood samples from several African nations from as early as 1959. HIV's mode of infection is described overleaf and its origin and prevalence are covered in the next activity.

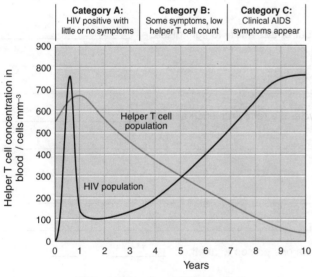

Capsid
Protein coat that protects the nucleic acids (RNA) within.

Viral envelope
A piece of the cell membrane budded off from the last human host cell.

Nucleic acid
Two identical strands of RNA contain the genetic blueprint for making more HIV viruses.

Reverse transcriptase
Two copies of this important enzyme convert the RNA into DNA once inside a host cell.

Surface proteins
These spikes allow HIV to attach to receptors on the host cells (T cells and macrophages).

The structure of HIV

HIV/AIDS

Individuals affected by the human immunodeficiency virus (HIV) may have no symptoms, while medical examination may detect swollen lymph glands. Others may experience a short-lived illness when they first become infected (resembling infectious mononucleosis). The range of symptoms resulting from HIV infection is huge, and is not the result of the HIV infection directly. The symptoms arise from an onslaught of secondary infections that gain a foothold in the body due to the suppressed immune system (due to the few helper T cells). These infections are from normally rare fungal, viral, and bacterial sources. Full blown AIDS can also feature some rare forms of cancer. Some symptoms are listed below:

Fever, lymphoma (cancer) and toxoplasmosis of the brain, dementia.

Eye infections (*Cytomegalovirus*).

Skin inflammation (dermatitis) particularly affecting the face.

Oral thrush (*Candida albicans*) of the oesophagus, bronchi, and lungs.

A variety of opportunistic infections, including: chronic or persistent *Herpes simplex*, tuberculosis (TB), pneumocystis pneumonia, shingles, shigellosis and salmonellosis.

Diarrhoea caused by *Isospora* or *Cryptosporidium*.

Marked weight loss.
A number of autoimmune diseases, especially destruction of platelets.

Kaposi's sarcoma: a highly aggressive malignant skin tumour consisting of blue-red nodules, usually start at the feet and ankles, spreading to the rest of the body later, including respiratory and gastrointestinal tracts.

Category A: HIV positive with little or no symptoms	Category B: Some symptoms, low helper T cell count	Category C: Clinical AIDS symptoms appear

Graph: Helper T cell concentration in blood / cells mm^{-3} (y-axis, 0 to 900) versus Years (x-axis, 0 to 10), showing Helper T cell population and HIV population.

The stages of an HIV infection

AIDS is actually only the end stage of an HIV infection. Shortly after the initial infection, HIV antibodies appear within the blood. The progress of infection has three clinical categories shown on the graph above.

1. Explain what is meant by **HIV positive**: _____

_____

2. Consult the graph above showing the stages of HIV infection (remember, HIV infects and destroys helper T cells).

(a) Describe how the virus population changes with the progression of the disease: _____

_____

_____

(b) Describe how the helper T cells respond to the infection: _____

_____

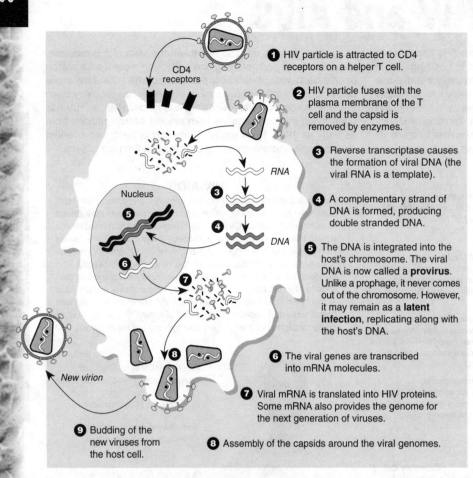

1. HIV particle is attracted to CD4 receptors on a helper T cell.

2. HIV particle fuses with the plasma membrane of the T cell and the capsid is removed by enzymes.

3. Reverse transcriptase causes the formation of viral DNA (the viral RNA is a template).

4. A complementary strand of DNA is formed, producing double stranded DNA.

5. The DNA is integrated into the host's chromosome. The viral DNA is now called a **provirus**. Unlike a prophage, it never comes out of the chromosome. However, it may remain as a **latent infection**, replicating along with the host's DNA.

6. The viral genes are transcribed into mRNA molecules.

7. Viral mRNA is translated into HIV proteins. Some mRNA also provides the genome for the next generation of viruses.

8. Assembly of the capsids around the viral genomes.

9. Budding of the new viruses from the host cell.

Modes of Transmission

1. HIV is transmitted in blood, vaginal secretions, semen, breast milk, and across the placenta.

2. In developed countries, blood transfusions are no longer a likely source of infection because blood is tested for HIV antibodies.

3. Historically, transmission of HIV in developed countries has been primarily through intravenous drug use and homosexual activity, but heterosexual transmission is increasing.

4. Transmission via heterosexual activity is important in Asia and Africa.

Treatment and Prevention

HIV's ability to destroy, evade, and hide inside cells of the human immune system make it difficult to treat. Research into conventional and extremely unconventional approaches to **vaccination** and **chemotherapy** is taking place. The first chemotherapy drug to show promise was *AZT*, which is a nucleotide analogue that inhibits reverse transcriptase. Protease inhibitors (Saquinavir, Ritonavir, Indinavir) are drugs that work by blocking the HIV protease. Once this is blocked, HIV makes copies of itself that cannot infect other cells. These drugs seem to be less toxic and to have less severe side effects than other anti-AIDS drugs. Subunit vaccines *HIVAC-1e* and *gp160* are being tested that use HIV glycoproteins inserted into other viruses.

3. Explain why the HIV virus has such a devastating effect on our body's ability to fight disease: _____

_____

_____

4. (a) Explain the role of the reverse transcriptase in the life cycle of a retrovirus such as HIV: _____

_____

_____

(b) Explain the significance of the formation of a provirus: _____

_____

5. Identify three ways in which HIV is commonly transmitted from one person to another: _____

_____

6. In the years immediately following the discovery of the HIV pathogen, there was a sudden appearance of AIDS cases amongst **haemophiliacs** (people with an inherited blood disorder). State why this group was being infected with HIV:

_____

_____

7. Explain why it has been so difficult to develop a **vaccine** against HIV: _____

_____

_____

8. In a rare number of cases, people who have been HIV positive for many years still have no apparent symptoms. Explain the significance of this observation and its likely potential in the search for a cure for AIDS:

_____

_____

Epidemiology of AIDS

In many urban centers of sub-Saharan Africa, Latin America, and the Caribbean, AIDS has already become the leading cause of death for both men and women aged 15 to 49 years. AIDS kills people in their most productive years and ranks as the leading cause of potential healthy life-years lost in sub-Saharan Africa. Within the next decade, crude death rates in some countries will more than double, and infant and child mortality rates will increase markedly. Perhaps the most significant impact will be seen in projected life expectancies due to the increased mortality of young adults. The AIDS pandemic has lowered the estimated world population level for the year 2050 from 9.4 billion to 8.9 billion – mostly caused by the massive toll of AIDS in Africa.

Infectious Disease

Regional HIV Statistics and Figures, December 2005

North America
People living with HIV / AIDS¶: 1.2 million
Adult prevalence rate*: 0.7%
People newly infected with HIV: 43 000
Deaths of people from AIDS: 18 000
Main modes of transmission**: MSM, IDU, Hetero

Western & Central Europe
People living with HIV / AIDS¶: 720 000
Adult prevalence rate*: 0.3%
People newly infected with HIV: 22 000
Deaths of people from AIDS: 12 000
Main modes of transmission**: Hetero, MSM, IDU

Eastern Europe & Central Asia
People living with HIV / AIDS¶: 1.6 million
Adult prevalence rate*: 0.9%
People newly infected with HIV: 270 000
Deaths of people from AIDS: 62 000
Main modes of transmission**: IDU, Hetero

Caribbean
People living with HIV / AIDS¶: 300 000
Adult prevalence rate*: 1.6%
People newly infected with HIV: 30 000
Deaths of people from AIDS: 24 000
Main modes of transmission**: Hetero, MSM, IDU

Latin America
People living with HIV / AIDS¶: 1.8 million
Adult prevalence rate*: 0.6%
People newly infected with HIV: 200 000
Deaths of people from AIDS: 66 000
Main modes of transmission**: Hetero, MSM, IDU

North Africa and Middle East
People living with HIV / AIDS¶: 510 000
Adult prevalence rate*: 0.2%
People newly infected with HIV: 67 000
Deaths of people from AIDS: 58 000
Main modes of transmission**: Hetero, IDU, MSM

Sub-Saharan Africa
People living with HIV / AIDS¶: 25.8 million
Adult prevalence rate*: 7.2%
People newly infected with HIV: 3.2 million
Deaths of people from AIDS: 2.4 million
Main modes of transmission**: Hetero

Oceania
People living with HIV / AIDS¶: 74 000
Adult prevalence rate*: 0.5%
People newly infected with HIV: 8200
Deaths of people from AIDS: 3600
Main modes of transmission**: MSM, Hetero, IDU

South & South East Asia
People living with HIV / AIDS¶: 7.4 million
Adult prevalence rate*: 0.7%
People newly infected with HIV: 990 000
Deaths of people from AIDS: 480 000
Main modes of transmission**: Hetero, IDU

East Asia
People living with HIV / AIDS¶: 870 000
Adult prevalence rate*: 0.1%
People newly infected with HIV: 140 000
Deaths of people from AIDS: 41 000
Main modes of transmission**: IDU, Hetero, MSM

Estimated percentage of adults (15-49) living with HIV/AIDS
- >15%
- 5 – 15%
- 0 – 5%

Source: UNAIDS, WHO

* The proportion of adults (15 to 49 years of age) living with HIV/AIDS in 2004   ¶ People includes adults & children
** Modes of transmission: **Hetero**: heterosexual sex; **IDU**: injecting drug use; **MSM**: sex between men

The origins of HIV

AIDS researchers have confirmed that the two strains of HIV each originated from cross-species transmission (**zoonosis**) from other primates. HIV-1, responsible for the global pandemic, arose as a result of recombination between two separate strains of simian immunodeficiency virus (SIV) in infected **common chimpanzees** in west-central Africa. HIV-2 is less virulent than HIV-1 and, until recently, was restricted to West Africa. It originated from a strain of SIV found in **sooty mangabey** monkeys in that region. The killing of primates as "bushmeat" for human consumption allows the virus to transmit to human hunters when they handle infected carcasses with cuts or other open wounds on their hands. Such cross-species transmissions could be happening every day.

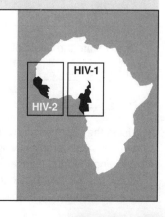

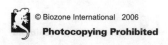

Code: DA 2

Factors in the spread of HIV

Epidemiologists cannot predict with certainty how rapidly a given epidemic will expand or when it will peak, although short term predictions can be made on the basis of trends in HIV spread and information on risk behaviour. Fortunately, there is strong evidence showing that countries will ultimately reduce their new infections if they carry out effective prevention programmes encouraging abstinence, or fidelity and safer sex. A crucial factor is promoting the acceptance and use of condoms, both the traditional kind and the female condom. Condoms are protective irrespective of age, the scope of sexual networks, or the presence of other sexually transmitted infections. There is evidence from around the world that many factors play a role in starting a sexually transmitted HIV epidemic or driving it to higher levels. Some of these risk factors are listed below.

In many African communities, men travel from rural settlements into the cities in search of work. These men often develop sexual networks while they are away and bring HIV with them when they return.

Social and behavioural risk factors
- Little or no condom use.
- Large proportion of the adult population with multiple partners.
- Overlapping (as opposed to serial) sexual partnerships. Individuals are highly infectious when they first acquire HIV and are more likely to infect any concurrent partners.
- Large sexual networks which are often seen in individuals who move back and forth between home and a far off work place.
- Women's economic dependence on marriage or prostitution, robbing them of control over the circumstances or safety of sex.

Biological risk factors
- High rates of sexually transmitted infections, especially those causing genital ulcers.
- Low rates of male circumcision (for poorly understood reasons, circumcised males have a reduced risk of contracting HIV).
- High viral load (HIV levels in the blood is typically highest when a person is first infected and again in the late stages of illness).

1. Comment on the social, economic, and biological factors involved in the prevalence of HIV in many of the **rural** communities of sub-Saharan Africa:

_____

_____

_____

_____

_____

2. Describe the effects of AIDS on the countries of sub-Saharan Africa with respect to the following:

(a) Age structure of their populations: _____

_____

(b) Their local economies: _____

_____

3. Effective antiviral therapies have reduced deaths from HIV/AIDS in developed countries. Suggest why a similar reduction has not occurred in the countries of sub-Saharan Africa:

_____

_____

4. Briefly state the origin of the two main strains of HIV:

HIV-1: _____

HIV-2: _____

5. Using the information provided on the opposite page and your own graph paper, plot a column graph of the number of males and females living with HIV/AIDS for each region. For example: to plot the data for Latin America, draw a bar showing the total number of people living with HIV/AIDS (1 700 000). Shade 36% (1 700 000 x 0.36 = 612 000) to show number of infected females. Shade the remaining 64% (1 700 000 x 0.64 =1 088 000) a different colour to show the infected males. Staple the completed graph into this workbook.

Bacterial Diseases

Of the many species of bacteria that exist in the world, relatively few cause disease in humans. The diagram below shows four adaptive features that help bacteria infect host tissue and cause disease. Bacteria infect a host to exploit the food potential of its body tissues. The fact that this exploitation causes disease is not in the interest of the bacteria; a healthy host is better than a sick one. Some human diseases caused by bacteria are illustrated in the diagram below. The natural reservoir (source of infection) of a disease varies from species to species, ranging from humans, insects, and other animals, to sewage and contaminated water.

Bacterial Infection

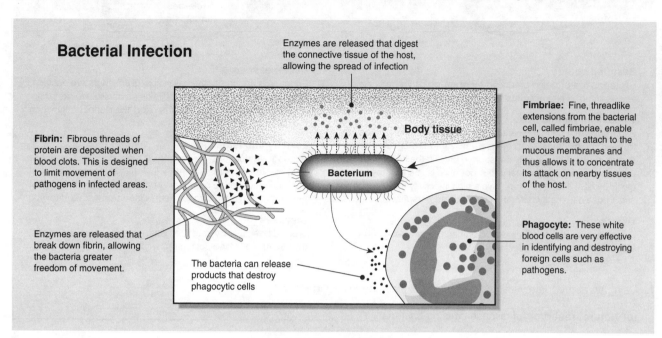

Enzymes are released that digest the connective tissue of the host, allowing the spread of infection

Body tissue

Fibrin: Fibrous threads of protein are deposited when blood clots. This is designed to limit movement of pathogens in infected areas.

Enzymes are released that break down fibrin, allowing the bacteria greater freedom of movement.

Bacterium

The bacteria can release products that destroy phagocytic cells

Fimbriae: Fine, threadlike extensions from the bacterial cell, called fimbriae, enable the bacteria to attach to the mucous membranes and thus allows it to concentrate its attack on nearby tissues of the host.

Phagocyte: These white blood cells are very effective in identifying and destroying foreign cells such as pathogens.

Examples of Bacterial Diseases

Streptococcus bacteria
These bacteria can cause scarlet fever, sore throats (pharyngitis) and a form of pneumonia. They exist as chains or in pairs. They cause more illness than any other group of bacteria.

Vibrio cholerae
These bacteria cause cholera, a disease common in Asia, caused by a temporary lapse in sanitation (where drinking water is contaminated with human waste).

Salmonella bacteria
This group is not divided up into species, but comprises over 2000 varieties (called *serovars*). They cause gastrointestinal diseases such as typhoid.

Staphylococcus aureus
This bacterium inhabits noses, the surface of skin, and is also found growing in cured meats such as ham. One of the most common causes of food poisoning, it produces many toxins that increase its ability to invade the body or damage tissue. It has the ability to develop antibiotic resistance very quickly and for this reason is a common problem in hospitals.

Enterobacter cloacae
This bacterium can cause urinary tract infections and is widely distributed in humans and animals, as well as in water, sewage and soil. It is a common source of hospital-acquired infection.

Haemophilus influenzae
Despite its name, this bacterium does not cause influenza. This organism inhabits the mucous membranes of the upper respiratory tract and mouth. It causes the most common form of meningitis in young children and is a frequent cause of earaches. It can also cause epiglottitis, bronchitis and pneumonia.

Yersinia pestis
This bacterium caused the Black Death or the bubonic plague of mediaeval Europe. Fleas from urban rats and ground squirrels transmit the bacteria among animals and to humans. Direct contact with animals and respiratory droplets from infected people can be involved in transmission.

Treponema pallidum
This spirochaete bacterium causes syphilis and is transmitted through sexual intercourse. The helical shape allows it to move by a corkscrew rotation.

Neisseria gonorrhoeae
This bacterium exists in a paired arrangement and causes the sexually transmitted disease called gonorrhoea. The fimbriae enable the organism to attach to the mucous membranes of the vagina and urethra of the penis.

64

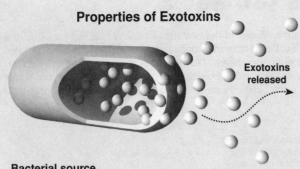

Properties of Exotoxins

Exotoxins released

Bacterial source
Exotoxins are proteins produced by **gram-positive** bacteria and released as part of normal bacterial growth and metabolism.

Toxicity and lethal dose
Exotoxins are amongst the most toxic compounds known. Due to their solubility they can diffuse easily into the circulatory system and are then easily transported around the body. They are unstable and can usually (but not always) be destroyed easily by heat. However, they have a high infectivity and a very small dose causes symptoms in the infected person.

Diseases
Gas gangrene, tetanus, botulism, diphtheria, scarlet fever, and various staphylococcal infections.

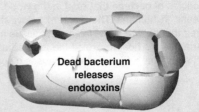

Properties of Endotoxins

Dead bacterium releases endotoxins

Bacterial source
Endotoxins are part of the cell wall of **gram-negative** bacteria. They are composed primarily of lipids (in contrast to exotoxins, which are proteins). Endotoxins exert their effect only when the bacteria die.

Toxicity and lethal dose
Although endotoxins are less toxic than exotoxins, they are heat stable and withstand autoclaving (121°C for one hour). The dose required to produce symptoms is relatively high, but the immune system cannot neutralise them with antitoxins.

Diseases
Typhoid fever, urinary tract infections, meningococcal meningitis, and *Salmonella* food poisoning.

1. Using an appropriate, illustrative example, explain the following terms:

   (a) **Natural reservoir** of disease-causing bacteria: _____

   _____

   (b) **Exotoxin**: _____

   _____

   (c) **Endotoxin**: _____

   _____

2. **Complete** the following table summarising the features of selected bacterial diseases. Use the illustration at the bottom of the previous page to assist you (for disease symptoms, consult a textbook, good dictionary, or an encyclopedia):

Bacteria	Natural reservoir	Diseases caused	Symptoms
(a) *Streptococcus* bacteria	Infected humans	Scarlet fever, sore throats, a form of pneumonia	Scarlet fever: fever, red tongue, rash on neck, chest, abdomen and limbs. Pneumonia: inflamed lungs with fluid in air sacs. Sore throat: inflammation of the throat.
(b) *Vibrio cholerae*			
(c) *Salmonella* bacteria	Common inhabitants of the guts of many animals (esp. poultry and cattle)		
(d) *Staphylococcus aureus*	Infected humans		
(e) *Enterobacter cloacae*			
(f) *Clostridium botulinum*		Botulism (a form of food poisoning)	
(g) *Yersinia pestis*			
(h) *Bacillus anthracis*		Anthrax	

Tuberculosis

Tuberculosis (TB) is a contagious disease caused by the *Mycobacterium tuberculosis* bacterium (**MTB**). The breakdown in health services in some countries, the spread of HIV/AIDS, and the emergence of **multidrug-resistant TB** are contributing to the increasingly harmful impact of this disease. In 1993, the World Health Organisation (WHO) responded to the growing pandemic and declared TB a global emergency. By 1998, the WHO estimated that about a third of the world's population were already infected with MTB. They estimate that 8 million new cases are added annually and that TB causes about 2 million deaths each year (note that in the figures given below, only *notified cases* are reported). If controls are not strengthened, it is anticipated that between 2002 and 2020, approximately 1000 million people will be newly infected, over 150 million people will get sick, and 36 million will die from TB.

Infection and Transmission

TB is a contagious disease, and is spread through the air when infectious people cough, sneeze, talk, or spit. A person needs only to inhale a small number of MTB to be infected.

Left untreated, each person with active TB will infect on average between 10 and 15 people every year. People infected with MTB will not necessarily get sick with the disease; the immune system 'walls off' the MTB which can lie dormant for years, protected by a thick waxy coat. When the immune system is weakened, the chance of getting sick (showing symptoms) is greater.

Symptoms

TB usually affects the lungs, but it can also affect other parts of the body, such as the brain, the kidneys, and the spine.

The general symptoms of TB disease include weakness and nausea, weight loss, fever, and night sweats. The symptoms of TB of the lungs include coughing, chest pain, and coughing up blood. The bacteria can spread from the bronchioles to other body systems, where the symptoms depend on the part of the body that is affected.

Treatment

TB is treated with an aggressive antibiotic regime. Since the early 1990s, the WHO has recommended the DOTS (Directly Observed Therapy, Short-course) strategy to control TB worldwide. This programme improves the proportion of patients successfully completing therapy (taking their full course of antibiotics). Proper completion of treatment is the most effective way in which to combat increasing drug resistance.

The Pathogenesis of Tuberculosis

The series below illustrates stages in MTB infection.

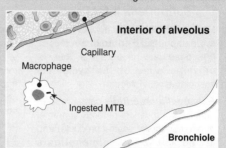

MTB enter the lung and are ingested by macrophages (phagocytic white blood cells).

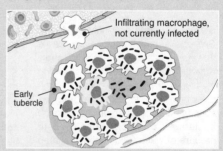

The multiplying bacteria cause the macrophages to swell and rupture. The newly released bacilli infect other macrophages. At this stage a tubercle may form and the disease may lie dormant.

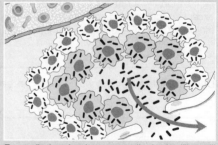

Eventually the tubercle ruptures, allowing bacilli to spill into the bronchiole. The bacilli can now be transmitted when the infected person coughs.

Estimated TB Incidence Rates in 2004 (cases per 100 000)

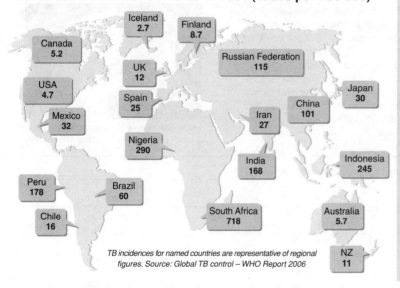

TB incidences for named countries are representative of regional figures. Source: Global TB control – WHO Report 2006

1. Identify the pathogen that causes tuberculosis (TB): _____

2. Explain how MTB may exist in a dormant state in a person for many years without causing disease symptoms:

   _____

   _____

3. State how TB is transmitted between people: _____

   _____

4. Suggest how some strains of MTB have acquired **multi-drug resistance**: _____

   _____

   _____

Foodborne Disease

Foodborne disease is caused by consuming contaminated foods or beverages. More than 250 food and waterborne diseases have been identified. The symptoms and severity of these vary according to the infectious agent, although diarrhoea and vomiting are two universal symptoms. Food poisoning is a term used for any gastrointestinal illness with sudden onset, usually accompanied by stomach pain, diarrhoea, and vomiting, and caused by eating **contaminated food**. It is a common cause of **gastroenteritis**. Food and waterborne diseases cause an estimated 76 million illnesses annually in the USA alone, although as many as 20% of these are probably acquired abroad. Such illnesses usually result from food contaminated with viruses, or bacteria or their toxins. They may also result from contamination of food or water by chemicals such as nitrates.

Common Sources of Bacterial Food Poisoning

Salmonella Infections

Most serotypes of *Salmonella* bacteria are pathogenic. **Endotoxins** released from dead bacteria are a likely (but not proven) cause of the symptoms associated with infection.

Salmonella enteritidis can spread to humans via a variety of foods of animal origin (especially poultry products) and is the cause of **salmonellosis** (*Salmonella* food poisoning). Typical symptoms include fever, accompanied by diarrhoea and abdominal cramps.

Salmonella typhi is a highly pathogenic *Salmonella* serotype and causes the life threatening disease, **typhoid fever**. *S.typhi* lives in humans and is shed in the faeces. Transmission occurs through the ingestion of food or drink that has been handled by a person shedding the bacterium, or when water used to prepare of wash food is contaminated with sewage containing the pathogen. Recovered patients can become carriers and continue to shed the bacteria and spread infection. Typhoid fever is common in most regions of the world except in industrialised nations such as the USA, Canada, and western Europe.

E. coli Gastroenteritis

Escherichia coli is the most common form of infantile and travellers' diarrhoea in developing countries. *E. coli* is the most abundant microbe in the intestinal tract and is normally harmless. However, certain strains are pathogenic and have specialised fimbriae allowing them to bind to the intestinal epithelial cells. They also release **exotoxins** which cause the production of copious watery diarrhoea and symptoms similar to mild cholera. *E. coli* infection is caused by poor sanitation and can be very difficult to avoid in developing countries.

Staphylococcus aureus

S. aureus is a normal inhabitant of human nasal passages. From here, it can contaminate the hands, where it may cause skin lesions and/or contaminate food. Contaminated food held at room temperature will rapidly produce a population of about 1 million bacteria per gram of food and enough **exotoxin** to cause illness. Unusually, the toxin is heat stable and can survive up to 30 minutes of boiling. Reheating the contaminated food may destroy the bacteria but not the toxin itself.

Faecal contamination of the hands at meal times is a common cause of gastroenteritis.

Sharing food and utensils may transmit foodborne pathogens between individuals.

Inadequate supply of clean drinking water is a major problem in many parts of the world.

1. Describe three ways in which food can become contaminated by *E. coli*: _____

_____

_____

2. Describe why food poisoning is more prevalent in developing countries: _____

_____

_____

3. Outline the basic precautions that should be taken with drinking water when travelling to developing countries:

_____

_____

4. (a) Describe the symptoms of salmonellosis: _____

_____

(b) Identify the method of transmission of this disease: _____

5. Explain why reheating food will still cause food poisoning if the food is contaminated with *Staphylococcus aureus*:

_____

Cholera

Cholera is an acute intestinal infection caused by the bacterium *Vibrio cholerae*. The disease has a short incubation period, from one to five days. The bacterium produces an enterotoxin that causes a copious, painless, watery diarrhoea that can quickly lead to severe dehydration and death if treatment is not promptly given. Most people infected with *V. cholerae* do not become ill, although the bacterium is present in their faeces for 7-14 days. When cholera appears in a community it is essential to take measures against its spread. These include: **hygienic disposal of human faeces**, provision of an adequate supply of **safe drinking water**, **safe food handling and preparation** (e.g. preventing contamination of food and cooking food thoroughly), and **effective general hygiene** (e.g. hand washing with soap). Cholera has reemerged as a global health threat after virtually disappearing from the Americas and most of Africa and Europe for more than a century. Originally restricted to the Indian subcontinent, cholera spread to Europe in 1817 in the first of seven pandemics. The current pandemic (below) shows signs of slowly abating, although under-reporting is a problem.

Symptoms

More than 90% of cases are of mild or moderate severity and are difficult to distinguish from other types of acute diarrhoea. Less than 10% of ill people develop typical cholera with signs of moderate or severe dehydration.

Treatment

Most cases of diarrhoea can be treated by giving a solution of oral rehydration salts. During an epidemic, 80-90% of diarrhoea patients can be treated by oral rehydration alone, but patients who become severely dehydrated must be given intravenous fluids. In severe cases, antibiotics can reduce the volume and duration of diarrhoea and reduce the presence of *V. cholerae* in the faeces.

Transmission

Cholera is spread by contaminated water and food. Sudden large outbreaks are usually caused by a contaminated water supply. *Vibrio cholerae* is often found in the aquatic environment and is part of the normal flora of brackish water and estuaries. Human beings are also one of the reservoirs of the pathogenic form of *Vibrio cholerae*.

The Cholera Pandemic: Reported Cases and Deaths (2004)

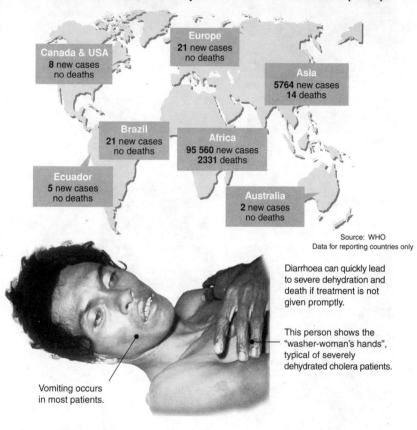

Europe
21 new cases
no deaths

Canada & USA
8 new cases
no deaths

Asia
5764 new cases
14 deaths

Brazil
21 new cases
no deaths

Africa
95 560 new cases
2331 deaths

Ecuador
5 new cases
no deaths

Australia
2 new cases
no deaths

Source: WHO
Data for reporting countries only

Diarrhoea can quickly lead to severe dehydration and death if treatment is not given promptly.

This person shows the "washer-woman's hands", typical of severely dehydrated cholera patients.

Vomiting occurs in most patients.

1. Name the pathogen that causes cholera: _____

2. (a) Describe the symptoms of cholera: _____

   _____

   (b) Explain why these symptoms are so dangerous if not treated quickly: _____

   _____

3. State how cholera is transmitted between people: _____

   _____

4. Describe the effective treatment of cholera at the following stages in the progression of the disease:

   (a) Mild onset of dehydration: _____

   (b) Severe symptoms: _____

5. Identify the risk factors associated with the incidence of cholera and relate these to social and economic conditions:

   _____

   _____

   _____

Fungal Diseases

The study of fungi (moulds, yeasts, and fleshy fungi) is called **mycology**. All fungi are chemoheterotrophs, requiring organic compounds for energy and carbon. Most fungi are saprophytes, and are found in the soil and water, where they decompose organic matter using extracellular enzymes. Of the 100 000 species of fungi, only about 100 species are pathogenic to humans and other animals, although thousands of fungal species are pathogenic to plants. Any fungal infection is called a **mycosis**. They are generally **chronic** (long-lasting) infections because fungi grow relatively slowly. Fungal infections are divided into three groups according to the degree of tissue involvement and the mode of entry into the host. Characteristics of these groups are summarised in the diagram below. Some of these infections (e.g. candidiasis) can also be classed opportunistic, because they occur when the host is immune depressed or weakened in some way.

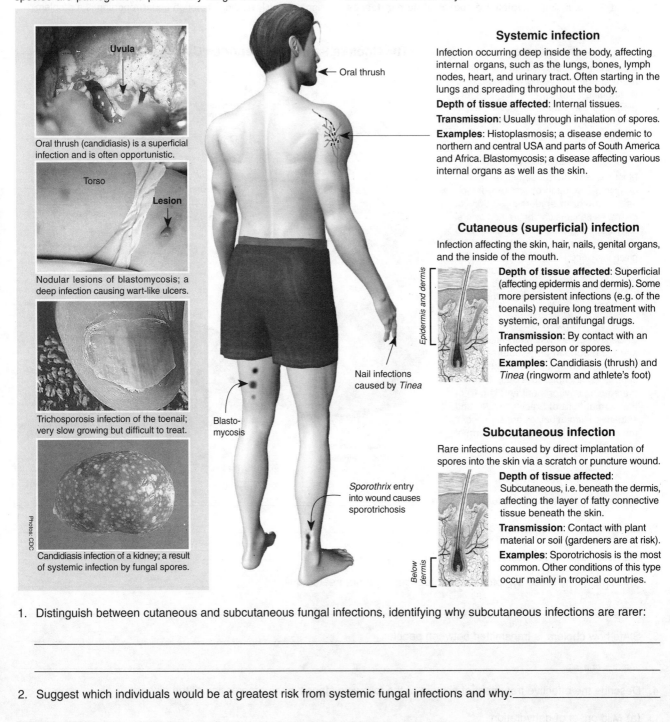

Uvula

Oral thrush (candidiasis) is a superficial infection and is often opportunistic.

Torso

Lesion

Nodular lesions of blastomycosis; a deep infection causing wart-like ulcers.

Trichosporosis infection of the toenail; very slow growing but difficult to treat.

Candidiasis infection of a kidney; a result of systemic infection by fungal spores.

Photos: CDC

Oral thrush

Blasto-mycosis

Nail infections caused by *Tinea*

Epidermis and dermis

Below dermis

Sporothrix entry into wound causes sporotrichosis

Systemic infection

Infection occurring deep inside the body, affecting internal organs, such as the lungs, bones, lymph nodes, heart, and urinary tract. Often starting in the lungs and spreading throughout the body.

Depth of tissue affected: Internal tissues.

Transmission: Usually through inhalation of spores.

Examples: Histoplasmosis; a disease endemic to northern and central USA and parts of South America and Africa. Blastomycosis; a disease affecting various internal organs as well as the skin.

Cutaneous (superficial) infection

Infection affecting the skin, hair, nails, genital organs, and the inside of the mouth.

Depth of tissue affected: Superficial (affecting epidermis and dermis). Some more persistent infections (e.g. of the toenails) require long treatment with systemic, oral antifungal drugs.

Transmission: By contact with an infected person or spores.

Examples: Candidiasis (thrush) and *Tinea* (ringworm and athlete's foot)

Subcutaneous infection

Rare infections caused by direct implantation of spores into the skin via a scratch or puncture wound.

Depth of tissue affected: Subcutaneous, i.e. beneath the dermis, affecting the layer of fatty connective tissue beneath the skin.

Transmission: Contact with plant material or soil (gardeners are at risk).

Examples: Sporotrichosis is the most common. Other conditions of this type occur mainly in tropical countries.

1. Distinguish between cutaneous and subcutaneous fungal infections, identifying why subcutaneous infections are rarer:

_____

_____

2. Suggest which individuals would be at greatest risk from systemic fungal infections and why:_____

_____

_____

3. Explain why fungal infections tend to be **chronic**:_____

_____

4. Suggest how the spread of athlete's foot (*Tinea pedis*) can be limited by thorough drying of the feet: _____

_____

Protozoan Diseases

Protozoa are one-celled, eukaryotic organisms that belong to the Kingdom Protista (Protoctista). Among the protozoans, there are many variations on cell structure. While most inhabit water and soil habitats, some are part of the natural microbiota of animals (i.e. they are microorganisms that live on or in animals). Relatively few of the nearly 20 000 species of protozoans cause disease; those that do are often highly specialised, intracellular parasites with complex life cycles involving one or more hosts. Under certain adverse conditions, some protozoans produce a protective capsule called a **cyst**. A cyst allows the protozoan to survive conditions unsuitable for survival. For specialised parasitic species, this includes survival for periods outside a host.

AMOEBAE

Amoebae move by extending projections of their cytoplasm. Several pathogenic amoebae infect humans and feed mainly on red blood cells. *Entamoeba* is transmitted through ingestion of cysts that are passed in the faeces. People become infected with *Naegleria* while swimming, when the waterborne cysts pass across mucous membranes and infect blood, brain, and spinal cord.

Pathogen	Disease
Naegleria fowleri	Microencephalitis
Entamoeba histolytica	Amoebic dysentery

MICROSPORA

This unusual group of protozoans lack mitochondria and live as intracellular parasites (within cells). They were first reported to cause human diseases in 1984.

Pathogen	Disease
Nosema	Chronic diarrhoea, kerato-conjunctivitis (in AIDS patients)

FLAGELLATES

Flagellates are usually spindle-shaped, with flagella projecting from the front end. The whiplike motion of the flagella pulls the cells through their environment. *Giardia* is found in the small intestine of mammals. It is passed in the faeces and survives in the environment as a cyst until ingested by the next host. *Trichinomas* moves using an undulating membrane. It is unable to form a cyst and must be transferred directly from host to host quickly (e.g. during sexual intercourse or via toilet facilities or towels). Various *Trypanosoma* species, which cause African sleeping sickness, are spread by the tsetse fly.

Pathogen	Disease
Giardia lamblia	Giardia enteritis
Trichinomas vaginalis	Urethritis, vaginitis
Trypanosoma (in tsetse fly vector)	Sleeping sickness (African trypanosomiasis)

APICOMPLEXA

These protozoans are not mobile and tend to be intracellular parasites. They use special enzymes to penetrate the host's tissues. They have complex life cycles involving transmission between several host species.

Plasmodium vivax

Pathogen	Disease	Host species
Plasmodium vivax	Malaria	*Anopheles* mosquito
Toxoplasma gondii	Toxoplasmosis	Cats
Pneumocystis carinii	Pneumonia	Humans

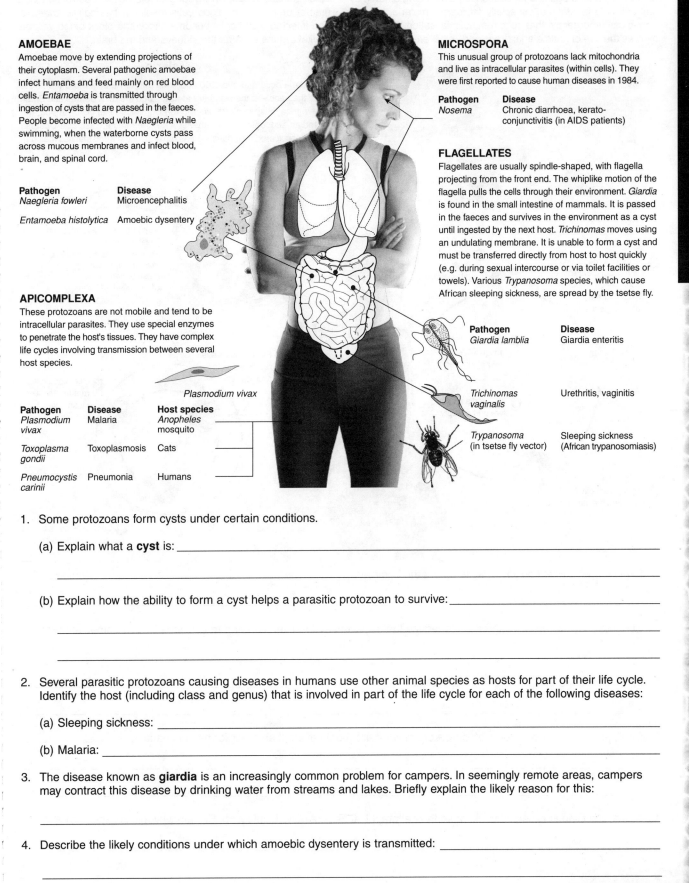

1. Some protozoans form cysts under certain conditions.

   (a) Explain what a **cyst** is: _____

   _____

   (b) Explain how the ability to form a cyst helps a parasitic protozoan to survive: _____

   _____

   _____

2. Several parasitic protozoans causing diseases in humans use other animal species as hosts for part of their life cycle. Identify the host (including class and genus) that is involved in part of the life cycle for each of the following diseases:

   (a) Sleeping sickness: _____

   (b) Malaria: _____

3. The disease known as **giardia** is an increasingly common problem for campers. In seemingly remote areas, campers may contract this disease by drinking water from streams and lakes. Briefly explain the likely reason for this:

   _____

4. Describe the likely conditions under which amoebic dysentery is transmitted: _____

   _____

Malaria

Malaria is a serious parasitic disease, spread by bites of **Anopheles mosquitoes**, affecting up to 300 million people in the tropics each year. The parasites responsible for malaria are protozoa known as **plasmodia**. Four species can cause the disease in humans. Each spends part of its life cycle in humans and part in *Anopheles* mosquitoes. Even people who take antimalarial drugs and precautions against being bitten may contract malaria. Malaria, especially *falciparum* malaria, is often a medical emergency that requires hospitalisation. Treatment involves the use of antimalarial drugs and, in severe cases, blood transfusions may be necessary. Symptoms, which appear one to two weeks after being bitten, include headache, shaking, chills, and fever. *Falciparum* malaria is more severe, with high fever, coma, and convulsions, and it can be fatal within a few days of the first symptoms. These more severe symptoms result from this plasmodium's ability to infect all ages of red blood cells (whereas other species attack only young or old cells). Destruction of a greater proportion of blood cells results in *haemolytic anaemia*. The infected blood cells become sticky and block blood vessels to vital organs such as the kidneys and the brain.

Malaria

Malaria occurs in over 100 countries and territories. More than 40% of the people in the world are at risk. Large areas of Central and South America, Hispaniola (Haiti and the Dominican Republic), Africa, the Indian subcontinent, Southeast Asia, the Middle East, and Oceania are considered malaria-risk areas (an area of the world that has malaria).

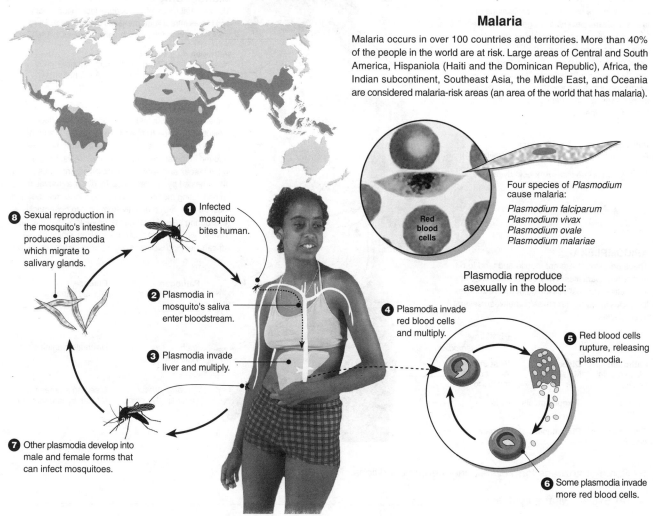

8 Sexual reproduction in the mosquito's intestine produces plasmodia which migrate to salivary glands.

1 Infected mosquito bites human.

2 Plasmodia in mosquito's saliva enter bloodstream.

3 Plasmodia invade liver and multiply.

7 Other plasmodia develop into male and female forms that can infect mosquitoes.

Red blood cells

Four species of *Plasmodium* cause malaria:

Plasmodium falciparum
Plasmodium vivax
Plasmodium ovale
Plasmodium malariae

Plasmodia reproduce asexually in the blood:

4 Plasmodia invade red blood cells and multiply.

5 Red blood cells rupture, releasing plasmodia.

6 Some plasmodia invade more red blood cells.

1. Explain how a *Plasmodium* parasite enters the body: _____

_____

2. Suggest a way in which villagers could reduce the occurrence of malaria carrying mosquitoes in their immediate area:

_____

3. (a) Describe the symptoms of a malaria attack: _____

_____

   (b) Explain why the symptoms of *falciparum* malaria are more severe than other forms of malaria: _____

_____

4. Global warming is expected to increase the geographical area of malaria infection. Explain why this is expected:

_____

Multicellular Parasites

Multicellular parasites comprise more than a single cell and are relatively complex organisms. Some **endoparasites**, such as flatworms and roundworms, cause disease directly and are highly specialised to live inside their hosts. Parasitic forms differ from their free-living relatives in the following ways: they have no digestive system or one that is highly simplified, their nervous system is reduced, they have little or no means of locomotion, and their reproductive system is often complex, with an individual producing large numbers of fertilised eggs to infect a new host. Some insects and arachnids (especially ticks and mites), apart from being **ectoparasites**, can also carry disease-causing microorganisms between hosts. They act as **vectors**, picking up bacteria, viruses, or protozoans when they suck the blood of their host. Some vectors are just a mechanical means of transport for a pathogen. Other parasites multiply in their vectors and can accumulate in the vector's saliva or faeces.

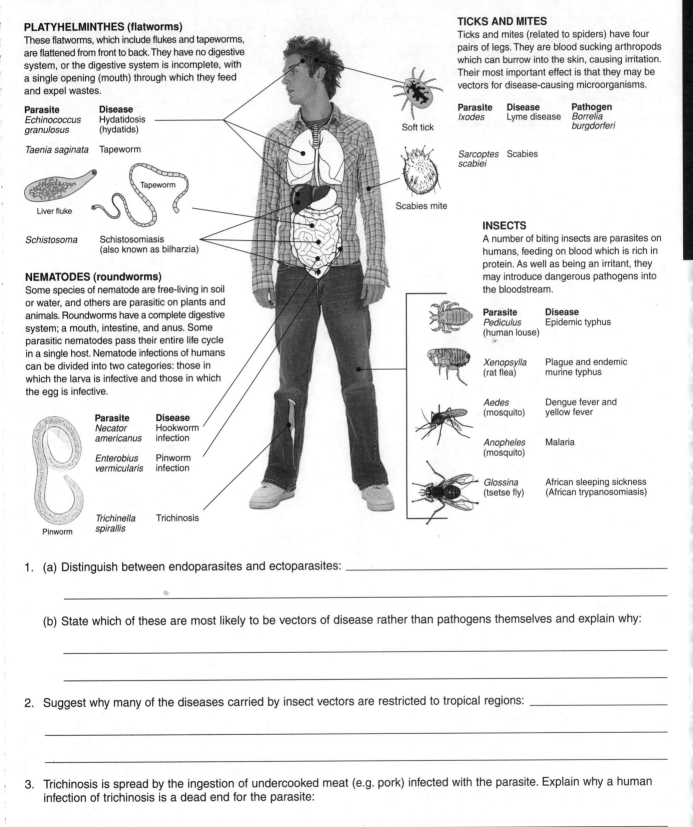

PLATYHELMINTHES (flatworms)

These flatworms, which include flukes and tapeworms, are flattened from front to back. They have no digestive system, or the digestive system is incomplete, with a single opening (mouth) through which they feed and expel wastes.

Parasite	Disease
Echinococcus granulosus	Hydatidosis (hydatids)
Taenia saginata	Tapeworm
Schistosoma	Schistosomiasis (also known as bilharzia)

Liver fluke

Tapeworm

NEMATODES (roundworms)

Some species of nematode are free-living in soil or water, and others are parasitic on plants and animals. Roundworms have a complete digestive system; a mouth, intestine, and anus. Some parasitic nematodes pass their entire life cycle in a single host. Nematode infections of humans can be divided into two categories: those in which the larva is infective and those in which the egg is infective.

Parasite	Disease
Necator americanus	Hookworm infection
Enterobius vermicularis	Pinworm infection
Trichinella spirallis	Trichinosis

Pinworm

TICKS AND MITES

Ticks and mites (related to spiders) have four pairs of legs. They are blood sucking arthropods which can burrow into the skin, causing irritation. Their most important effect is that they may be vectors for disease-causing microorganisms.

Parasite	Disease	Pathogen
Ixodes	Lyme disease	*Borrelia burgdorferi*
Sarcoptes scabiei	Scabies	

Soft tick

Scabies mite

INSECTS

A number of biting insects are parasites on humans, feeding on blood which is rich in protein. As well as being an irritant, they may introduce dangerous pathogens into the bloodstream.

Parasite	Disease
Pediculus (human louse)	Epidemic typhus
Xenopsylla (rat flea)	Plague and endemic murine typhus
Aedes (mosquito)	Dengue fever and yellow fever
Anopheles (mosquito)	Malaria
Glossina (tsetse fly)	African sleeping sickness (African trypanosomiasis)

1. (a) Distinguish between endoparasites and ectoparasites: _____

_____

(b) State which of these are most likely to be vectors of disease rather than pathogens themselves and explain why:

_____

_____

2. Suggest why many of the diseases carried by insect vectors are restricted to tropical regions: _____

_____

_____

3. Trichinosis is spread by the ingestion of undercooked meat (e.g. pork) infected with the parasite. Explain why a human infection of trichinosis is a dead end for the parasite:

_____

_____

Code: RA 3

4. Explain why tapeworms, as a result of their parasitic way of life, have the following special features:

(a) No digestive system: _____

_____

_____

(b) No means of locomotion: _____

_____

_____

(c) Reduced nervous system: _____

_____

_____

5. Draw a diagram to summarise the life cycle of the parasite **hydatid tapeworm**:

The Schistosoma Parasite

Infectious Disease

Some **endoparasites**, such as flatworms and roundworms, cause disease directly and are highly specialised to live inside their hosts. Schistosomes, or blood flukes, are specialised parasitic **trematode flatworms** of the genus *Schistosoma*. They are found as adults in the blood vessels of their mammalian hosts and cause the disease **schistosomiasis**, one of the most widespread and devastating parasitic diseases of humans. It is endemic in 74 developing countries with more than 80% of infected people living in sub-Saharan Africa. Unlike most other

flukes, schistosomes have separate sexes, and the female and male remain clasped together for their entire reproductive life. Transmission of the *Schistosoma* parasite occurs in freshwater when intermediate snail hosts release infective larval forms of the parasite (cercariae). In intestinal schistosomiasis, there is progressive enlargement of the spleen and liver, and intestinal damage and bleeding. The disease has a low fatality rate, but a high morbidity. Sufferers become severely weakened and liver, spleen, and kidney function become impaired.

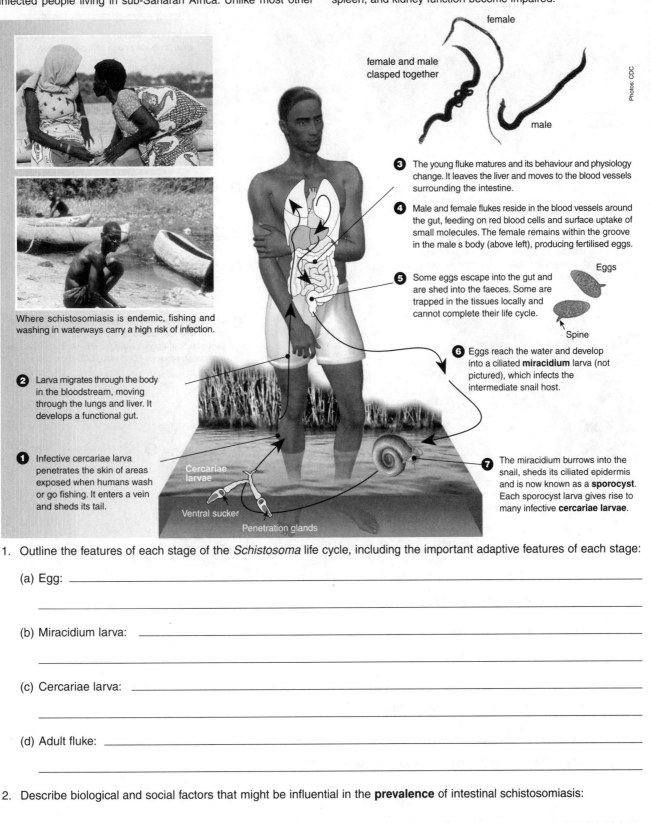

Where schistosomiasis is endemic, fishing and washing in waterways carry a high risk of infection.

1. Outline the features of each stage of the *Schistosoma* life cycle, including the important adaptive features of each stage:

(a) Egg: _____

(b) Miracidium larva: _____

(c) Cercariae larva: _____

(d) Adult fluke: _____

2. Describe biological and social factors that might be influential in the **prevalence** of intestinal schistosomiasis:

Hookworm Infection

Hookworm infestations affect about 700 million people worldwide, mainly those living in the tropics, and were once very common in the south-western states of the USA. With improved sanitation, its incidence has declined greatly. There are two species of hookworm: *Ancylostoma duodenale* and *Necator americanus*.

Collectively they perform the equivalent of draining the blood from some 1.5 million people every day. Antihelminthic drugs, such as mebendazole, kill the worms but only effective sanitation can eliminate the disease. The diagram below illustrates the life cycle and distribution of *Necator americanus*.

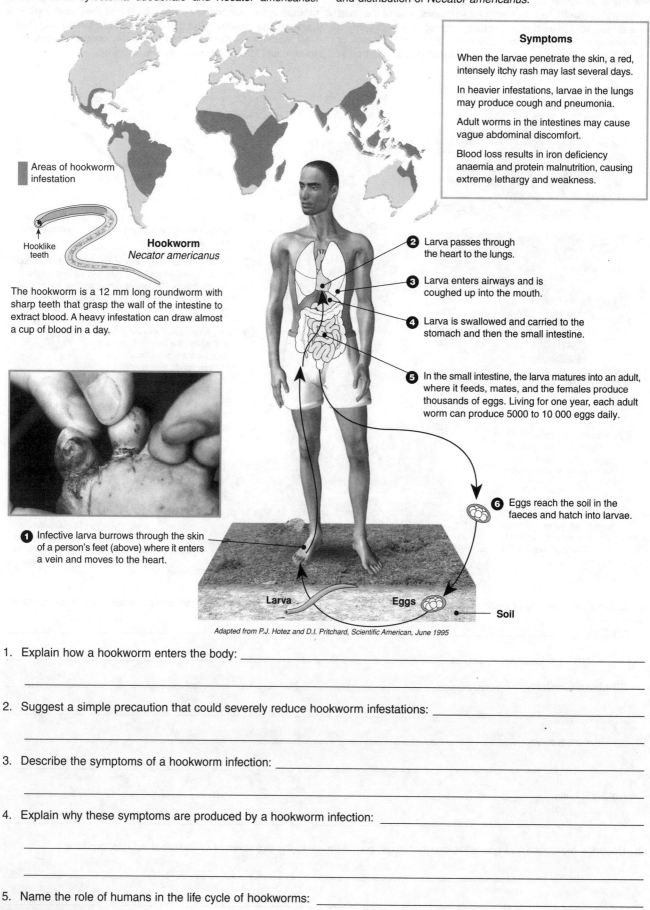

Areas of hookworm infestation

Hookworm
Necator americanus

Hooklike teeth

The hookworm is a 12 mm long roundworm with sharp teeth that grasp the wall of the intestine to extract blood. A heavy infestation can draw almost a cup of blood in a day.

Symptoms

When the larvae penetrate the skin, a red, intensely itchy rash may last several days.

In heavier infestations, larvae in the lungs may produce cough and pneumonia.

Adult worms in the intestines may cause vague abdominal discomfort.

Blood loss results in iron deficiency anaemia and protein malnutrition, causing extreme lethargy and weakness.

2 Larva passes through the heart to the lungs.

3 Larva enters airways and is coughed up into the mouth.

4 Larva is swallowed and carried to the stomach and then the small intestine.

5 In the small intestine, the larva matures into an adult, where it feeds, mates, and the females produce thousands of eggs. Living for one year, each adult worm can produce 5000 to 10 000 eggs daily.

6 Eggs reach the soil in the faeces and hatch into larvae.

1 Infective larva burrows through the skin of a person's feet (above) where it enters a vein and moves to the heart.

Larva   Eggs   Soil

Adapted from P.J. Hotez and D.I. Pritchard, *Scientific American*, June 1995

1. Explain how a hookworm enters the body: _____

_____

2. Suggest a simple precaution that could severely reduce hookworm infestations: _____

_____

3. Describe the symptoms of a hookworm infection: _____

_____

4. Explain why these symptoms are produced by a hookworm infection: _____

_____

_____

5. Name the role of humans in the life cycle of hookworms: _____

Code: A 2

Prion Diseases

Until recently, all pathogens were thought to contain some form of nucleic acid. It now seems possible that a protein alone can be an infectious agent. Called **prions**, they are capable of replication and of causing infection. Prions have been spread by eating contaminated meat and, because they resist normal sterilisation methods, they can be spread on surgical instruments. Prions are produced by mutations in the gene coding for a normal cell protein (PrP). They cause a group of degenerative nervous diseases in mammals called transmissible spongiform encephalopathies (TSE). These include scrapie in sheep, bovine spongiform encephalopathy (**BSE**) in cattle, and variant **Creutzfeldt-Jakob disease** and **kuru** in humans. Different mutations of the PrP gene are thought to be responsible in each case.

The Infectious Nature of Prion Proteins

A shape change transforms the harmless protein into its infectious 'prion' form. This shape change may be caused by a point mutation in the gene that codes for it.

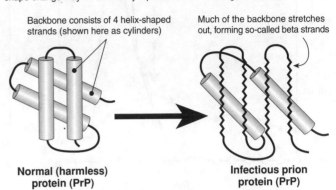

Backbone consists of 4 helix-shaped strands (shown here as cylinders)

Much of the backbone stretches out, forming so-called beta strands

Normal (harmless) protein (PrP)

Infectious prion protein (PrP)

Kuru is the condition which first brought prion diseases to prominence in the 1950s. Found in the geographically isolated tribes in the Fore highlands of Papua New Guinea. Researchers discovered that these people were eating the brain tissue of dead relatives for religious reasons. They ground up the brain into a pale grey soup, heated it and ate it. Clinically, the disease resembles CJD.

Propagation of the Prion Protein

Infectious protein (prion) has an unusual shape allowing it to bind to the normal form of the protein.

The normal (harmless) protein is converted into the infectious prion form.

The original and newly formed prions attack other normal proteins nearby. Those molecules, in turn, attack other normal molecules, until the prions accumulate to dangerous levels.

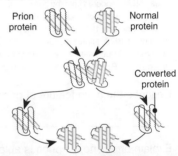

Prion protein

Normal protein

Converted protein

Prion diseases of selected mammals

Mammal	Disease
Sheep	Scrapie
Mink	Transmissible Mink Encephalopathy (TME)
Mule deer, elk	Chronic Wasting Disease (CWD)
Cattle	Bovine Spongiform Encephalopathy (BSE)

Prion Diseases of Humans

Disease	Typical symptoms	Acquisition of disease	Distribution	Span of overt illness
Kuru	Loss of coordination, often followed by dementia.	Infection probably through cannibalism (which stopped in 1958).	Known only in highlands of Papua New Guinea; some 2600 cases have been identified since 1957.	Three months to one year
"Classical" Creutzfeldt-Jakob Disease (CJD)	Dementia, followed by loss of coordination, although sometimes this sequence is reversed.	Usually unknown (in "sporadic" disease). In 10-15% of cases, inheritance of a mutation in the gene coding for the prion protein. Infection as an accidental consequence of surgery, as well as growth hormone injections, corneal transplants from dead donors (not blood transfusions).	*Sporadic form:* 1 person per million worldwide. *Inherited form:* some 100 extended families have been identified. *Infectious form:* 80 cases from medical procedures (e.g. injection of human growth hormone from pituitary of dead people).	Typically about one year; the range is one month to more than 10 years
Mad Cow Disease or Variant Creutzfeldt-Jakob Disease (vCJD)	Dementia, shaky movements, unsteady gait, sudden, jerky, involuntary movements of head, face, or limbs.	Infection by eating beef products from cattle infected with bovine spongiform encephalopathy (BSE).	By June 1999, 43 people had been identified as being infected from BSE cattle in the UK.	Unknown but probably between 2 and 30 years
Gerstmann-Straussler-Scheinker Disease (GSS)	Loss of coordination, often followed by dementia.	Inheritance of a mutation in the gene coding for the prion protein (PrP).	Some 50 extended families have been identified.	Typically about two to six years
Fatal Familial Insomnia	Trouble sleeping and disturbance of the autonomic nervous system, followed by insomnia and dementia.	Inheritance of a mutation in the gene coding for the prion protein (PrP).	Nine extended families have been identified.	Typically about one year

Source: Modified after Scientific American, January 1995, p. 32.

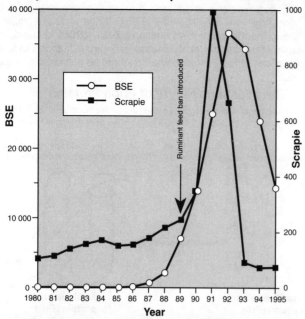

Reported incidence of scrapie and BSE in the UK

BSE / Scrapie graph. Legend: BSE (open circles), Scrapie (filled squares). "Ruminant feed ban introduced" marked by arrow. X-axis: Year 1980 81 82 83 84 85 86 87 88 89 90 91 92 93 94 1995. Left Y-axis: BSE 0 to 40 000. Right Y-axis: Scrapie 0 to 1000.

The first cases of Bovine Spongiform Encephalopathy (BSE) were seen at the end of 1986. The disease had spread because meat and bone meal (MBM) rendered from the bodies of infected cows and sheep (infected with a similar disease, scrapie), were used in feeds given to other cattle. On the 18th July 1988, Britain banned ruminant-to-ruminant feeding. By the end of 1998, approximately 170 000 cases had been confirmed and another 100 000 cattle were culled in an attempt to stop the spread of the disease. BSE very nearly destroyed the British beef industry.

Deaths of human prion disease cases in the UK

Year	Sporadic	Iatrogenic	Familial	GSS	vCJD	Total¶
1991	32	1	3	0	-	36
1992	45	2	5	1	-	53
1993	37	4	3	2	-	46
1994	53	1	4	3	-	61
1995	35	4	2	3	3	47
1996	40	4	2	4	10	60
1997	60	6	4	1	10	81
1998	63	3	3	2	18	89
1999	62	6	2	0	15	85
2000	50	1	2	1	28	82
2001	58	4	3	2	20	87
2002	72	0	4	1	17	94
2003	77	5	4	2	18	106
2004	52	2	3	1	9	67
2005	62	3	6	4	5	80
2006*	8	0	1	0	1	10

Source: Department of Health, United Kingdom: www.cjd.ed.ac.uk/figures.htm

Sporadic: Classic CJD cases that appear to occur spontaneously with no definite cause and account for 85% of all cases.

Iatrogenic: Classic CJD cases resulting from a medical procedure. All U.K. cases have resulted from treatment with human derived pituitary growth hormones or from grafts using dura mater (a membrane lining the skull).

Familial: Cases occurring in families associated with mutations in the PrP gene (10-15% of cases).

GSS: *Gertsmann-Straussler-Scheinker syndrome;* an extremely rare inherited autosomal dominant disease that causes shaky movements and terminal dementia.

vCJD: Variant CJD (originally named *new variant* CJD). Hitherto unrecognised variant of CJD discovered in April 1996.

Total¶: Includes all confirmed cases.

* Incomplete data (as to 29 March 2006)

1. Describe the main feature of prions that distinguishes them from other infectious agents: _____

_____

2. Explain briefly how a prion is able to replicate inside a mammal's body: _____

_____

_____

_____

3. In 1988, the British government introduced a ban on feeding cattle with meat and bone meal.

   (a) Explain the purpose of this ban: _____

   _____

   (b) Suggest why the incidence of **BSE** continued to increase for a number of years after the ban: _____

   _____

   _____

4. State the source of infection for people with **variant CJD**: _____

5. Describe the cultural practice of highland tribes of Papua New Guinea that spread the prion disease known as **kuru**:

_____

_____

6. Name a prion disease that affects the following mammals:

   (a) Sheep: _____   (b) Cattle: _____   (c) Humans: _____

7. Identify three medical procedures that have been known to accidentally introduce CJD into patients: _____

_____

Emerging Diseases

A host of infectious diseases new to humans have affected millions of people world-wide. These **emerging diseases** pose a real threat to the human population, particularly in some countries. Emerging diseases are so named because they have no previous history in the human population. Often, as with **AIDS** and **SARS**, they are **zoonoses** (animal diseases that cross to humans). Zoonoses are capable of causing highly lethal **pandemics** (world-wide epidemics) amongst an unprepared population. The increasing incidence of **drug-resistance** in pathogens (including those that cause tuberculosis, malaria, pneumonia, gonorrhea,

and cholera) has led to the **re-emergence** of diseases that were previously thought to be largely under control. Foodborne diseases are also on the rise, despite improved hygiene. Even diseases once thought to be non-infectious (e.g. stomach ulcers and cervical cancer) are now known to be linked to infectious agents. In the 1940s, many common and lethal diseases (e.g. scarlet fever and diphtheria) were conquered using antibiotics. It is now evident that antibiotics are not only losing their power, they are encouraging the emergence of deadly and untreatable infections.

E. coli 0157:H7

A highly pathogenic form of a normally harmless human intestinal bacterium, *Escherichia coli* (below), which causes diarrhoea, sweating, vomiting, and sometimes death. Past sources of contamination include meats (Scotland) and apple juice (western US). Several deaths in New York and Canada were caused by outbreaks of this pathogen in 1999-2000.

BSE and CJD

Investigation into the appearance of a new form of **Creutzfeldt-Jakob Disease** (vCJD) in Britain in 1994-1995 established a link with **Mad Cow Disease** or BSE (**bovine spongiform encephalopathy**). This **prion** disease is spread through the consumption of contaminated beef.

Severe Acute Respiratory Syndrome (SARS)

The first case of this respiratory illness was reported 16 November 2002, in China. Initially, epidemiologists thought that people were contracting SARS from eating masked palm civet and racoon-dogs infected with the virus. It is now known that the reservoir for the disease is a bat, which passes the infection to other mammals. Once in the human population, SARS spread rapidly through close contact (coughing and sneezing). The virus (right) belongs to a group called Coronaviruses. SARS had a mortality of about 10%, with 50% for people aged 60+.

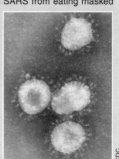

Resistant Tuberculosis

The reappearance of TB as a virulent disease is the result of an increasing multi-drug resistance to antibiotics and fewer people being immunised.

Hantavirus

An outbreak in Argentina of *hantavirus pulmonary syndrome* in 1996 caused 9 deaths from 17 cases. The source of infection was contact with rodent faeces. An outbreak in Panama, in 2000, caused 3 deaths.

Avian influenza A(H5N1)

In January 2004, a new strain of 'bird flu' (H5N1) spread rapidly through 8 Asian countries. Outbreaks occurred again in 2005, each time with high human mortality. It is now continuing its spread through Africa and Europe. Because it mutates rapidly and appears to easily cross the species barrier, this disease poses a considerable public health threat.

West Nile Virus

A sometimes fatal encephalitis caused by a flaviviral infection. Most of those infected have no symptoms, but 20% will have some symptoms and a small proportion (less than 1%) will develop severe infection. Symptoms of severe infection include high fever, coma, convulsions, and paralysis. In 2002, there were 277 deaths from West Nile fever in the US, with infection rates concentrated in certain states. The disease is transmitted to humans via **mosquitoes** (below), which are infected with the virus when feeding on bird **reservoir hosts**. Over 110 bird species are known to have been infected with West Nile virus, and bird deaths are closely monitored in the US as indicators of West Nile outbreaks.

Haemorrhagic Fevers: Ebola & Marburg

Viral haemorrhagic fevers are a group of diseases from four distinct families of viruses. The two best known examples are the filoviruses **Ebola** (below) and **Marburg**. Outbreaks of Ebola have occurred sporadically: in 1976 and 1979, and again in 1995-1996 and 2001-2003. Marburg virus erupted in Angola early in 2005 and continued through that year. Mortality was high at 87%, with a total of 276 of 316 reported cases being fatal.

HIV and AIDS

The AIDS pandemic is set to have a lasting effect on the world population. At least two strains are recognised: the deadly **HIV-1 virus** is more widespread than the slightly more benign **HIV-2 strain**. HIV viruses (arrowed) are shown below emerging from a human T cell. HIV is responsible for the massive AIDS pandemic that some claim to be species threatening.

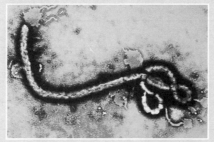

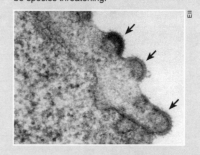

Code: RA 2

1. Describe the biological and social factors important in the emergence and spread of a named **emerging disease**:

   _____

   _____

   _____

   _____

   _____

2. Explain the role of **zoonoses** in the emergence of new diseases: _____

   _____

   _____

3. Using an example, explain what a **re-emerging disease** is: _____

   _____

   _____

4. Explain how drug resistance in pathogens has led to an increase in the number of re-emerging diseases:

   _____

   _____

   _____

5. Distinguish between an **epidemic** and a **pandemic**: _____

   _____

   _____

6. Describe the biological and social factors involved when diseases spread rapidly through hospitals: _____

   _____

   _____

   _____

7. The Spanish influenza pandemic of 1917-18 was made worse by the return of troops from World War I to their home countries. More than 20 million people died in the pandemic, which had a death rate of about 3%. Explain how this pandemic differed from that of SARS in 2003, in terms of its **global spread** and **death rate**:

   _____

   _____

   _____

8. The next pandemic may well be avian flu. Discuss why this disease poses such a public health threat and describe the precautions necessary in preventing its global spread:

   _____

   _____

   _____

   _____

   _____

   _____

Preventing and Treating Disease

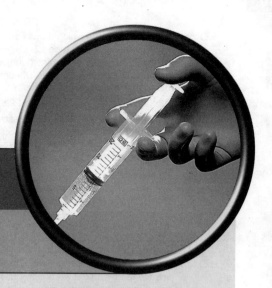

Diagnosing, treating, and preventing disease

Public health and quarantine. Vaccines and immunisation. Preventing lifestyle disease. Methods for diagnosing and treating disease.

Learning Objectives

☐ 1. Compile your own glossary from the **KEY WORDS** displayed in **bold type** in the learning objectives below.

Public Health & Quarantine *(pages 52-55, 91-92)*

☐ 2. Explain the importance of disease prevention to public health. Identify the role of (improved) **hygiene** and **sanitation** in controlling some infectious diseases. Discuss why disease prevention is more difficult where hygiene standards are poor and there is inadequate clean water.

☐ 3. Explain what is meant by **quarantine**. Explain the important role of quarantine measures in preventing the spread of disease between countries.

☐ 4. Distinguish between **antiseptics** and **disinfectants** and state their role in preventing the spread of disease. Explain the role of pesticides in controlling vector borne diseases (particularly in tropical countries).

☐ 5. Explain what is meant by a **public health programme**. Explain the role of such programmes in preventing disease. Outline the reliance of such programmes on public education and the availability of suitable facilities.

☐ 6. Explain the purpose of **health statistics** and describe the sort of information that they provide. Explain the role of health statistics in public health programmes.

Preventing Lifestyle Diseases *(pages 87-90)*

☐ 7. Discuss the role of diet, exercise, and stress relief in the prevention of some lifestyle diseases (e.g. obesity).

☐ 8. Explain what is meant by a **balanced diet** recognising the role of each of the following: proteins, fats, carbohydrates, vitamins, and minerals.

☐ 9. Discuss the energy and nutrient requirements of people with reference to gender, age, level of activity, pregnancy, and lactation. Describe the role of **Recommended Dietary Intakes** and their equivalents (e.g. **Recommended Daily Amounts** and **Dietary Reference Values**) in determining nutritional guidelines. Recognise that these values are country specific and are not necessarily always based on the same criteria.

Vaccines & Immunisation *(pages 23, 97-101)*

☐ 10. Review the distinction between passive and **active immunity**. Define the terms: **vaccine**, **immunity**, **vaccination** (= **immunisation**). Appreciate that **immunisation** involves the production of immunity by artificial means and that **vaccination** usually refers to immunisation by inoculation. Know that these terms are frequently used synonymously.

☐ 11. Explain how vaccination provides protection against disease. Discuss the role of modern **vaccination programmes** in preventing disease. Comment on the contribution of aggressive vaccination programmes to the eradication of some (named) infectious diseases. If required, outline the vaccination schedule for your country, identifying critical times for vaccination against specific diseases. Comment on the role of effective vaccination programmes in public health and the incidence of infectious disease.

☐ 12. Describe the principles involved in the production of vaccines. Giving examples, explain how vaccines are administered. Distinguish between **subunit** and **whole-agent vaccines** and between **inactivated** (dead) and **live** (attenuated) **vaccines**. Contrast the risks and benefits associated with live and dead vaccines.

☐ 13. Evaluate the risks associated with immunisation. Compare these risks with the risks associated with contracting the disease itself.

☐ 14. Describe and comment on the role of genetic engineering in the development of new vaccines.

Diagnosing Disease *(pages 81-86, 95-96, 103-104)*

☐ 15. Outline some of the technologies available for detecting and diagnosing diseases and homeostatic imbalances. Include any of: prenatal tests for inherited disorders (e.g. amniocentesis, CVS, ultrasound), postnatal tests, X-rays, CAT scans, MRI, biosensors.

☐ 16. Identify the role of the *Human Genome Project* in the further development of genetic screening programmes.

☐ 17. Explain what **monoclonal antibodies** are and explain how they are produced. Explain why they are so useful in medicine and outline some of their applications.

☐ 18. Describe the role of monoclonal antibodies in the diagnosis of disease. Recognise the application of monoclonal antibodies to the treatment of disease.

☐ 19. Outline the principles of **genetic counselling** and explain its role in the diagnosis of genetic disorders. Appreciate how this field has been expanded in the light of new technologies.

Treatment of Disease *(refer to pages listed below)*

Surgical treatments *(pages 37, 86, 109-112)*

☐ 20. Name some of the diseases that are most successfully treated with **surgery**. Using a named example, describe precisely how surgery is used to treat disease.

Therapeutic drugs *(pages 36-37, 91-94)*

☐ 21. Discuss the use of **therapeutic drugs**, including **antimicrobial drugs** and **chemotherapy**, in the treatment of infectious and non-infectious disease. Outline the importance of new drug technologies in the treatment of viral diseases such as HIV/AIDS.

22. Outline the ways in which drugs can work against:
    (a) Bacterial diseases (see #24).
    (b) Cancers (especially isolated tumours).
    (c) Autoimmune diseases (e.g. rheumatoid arthritis).
    (d) Allergic reactions (e.g. asthma).
    (e) Viral diseases (e.g. AIDS, herpes, hepatitis B).

23. Outline the history of **antibiotic** discovery and use. Describe the importance of antibiotics to modern medicine, identifying the group of organisms against which they are (and are not) effective.

24. Explain how an antibiotic works to prevent disease. Explain why particular antibiotics are effective against specific types of bacteria and not against others. Discuss the implications of **antibiotic resistance** to the continued, effective treatment of disease.

Radiotherapy *(pages 36-37)*

25. Discuss when and how radiation (**radiotherapy**) is used in the treatment of cancer. Outline the techniques and discuss the side effects associated with treatment.

Kidney dialysis *(page 115)*

26. Describe the technique and application of **kidney dialysis**. Explain how dialysis is used for restoring and maintaining homeostasis in cases of kidney failure.

Transplant technology *(pages 102, 109-114)*

27. Identify problems associated with the supply and transfusion of **blood** and blood products. Identify the need for an adequate blood substitute. Describe the problems associated with the production of **artificial blood**, outlining the reasons why blood is such a difficult product to produce by artificial means.

28. Describe the principles involved and the applications of **transplant technology**, including organ transplants. Outline the technical and ethical difficulties associated with the use of transplanted organs and tissues.

29. Describe the principles and techniques involved in **tissue engineering**. Discuss the benefits (including both the ethical and biological benefits) associated with the use of engineered tissues in medicine.

30. Explain what is meant by **stem cell technology**. Outline the properties of stem cells that make them potentially so useful in medicine and discuss their present and possible future applications.

Gene therapy *(pages 84, 103-108)*

31. Discuss the current and future role of **gene therapy** in treating disease. Explain the techniques involved in gene therapy and identify problems associated with these techniques and their application.

32. Identify the criteria that must be fulfilled in order for gene therapy to be feasible. Identify diseases that are suitable, or potentially suitable, for treatment with gene therapy.

33. Recognise the contribution of the **Human Genome Project** to the identification of diseases suitable for treatment by gene therapy methods.

Supplementary Texts

See page 7 for additional details of this text:

■ Chenn, P. 1997. **Microorganisms and Biotechnology** (John Murray), chpt. 8 & 9 as reqd.

■ Freeland, P., 1999. **Microbes, Medicine and Commerce** (Hodder & Stoughton), chpt. 6.

■ Fullick, A., 1998. **Human Health and Disease** (Heinemann), chpt. 1 & 3 as required.

■ Hudson, T. & K. Mannion, 2001. **Microbes and Disease** (Collins), chpt .6.

■ Murray, P. & N. Owens, 2001. **Behaviour and Populations** (Collins), chpt. 7-8.

■ Taylor, J., 2001. **Microorganisms and Biotechnology** (NelsonThornes), chpt. 7.

Periodicals

See page 7 for details of publishers of periodicals:

STUDENT'S REFERENCE

■ **Rebuilding the Food Pyramid** Scientific American, January 2003, pp. 52-59. *A major revision of the basic nutritional guidelines provided for consumers and health professionals. A critique of dietary information and an analysis of what we should be eating now (a good topic for debate).*

■ **Antibiotics** Biol. Sci. Rev. May 1999, pp. 18-20. *Antibiotics: how they were discovered and how they work to kill their target organisms.*

■ **Finding and Improving Antibiotics** Biol. Sci. Rev. 12(1) Sept. 1999, pp. 36-38. *Antibiotics, their production & testing, and the search for new drugs.*

■ **Antibiotic Resistance** Biol. Sci. Rev. Nov. 1999 pp. 28-30. *The incidence and mechanisms behind spontaneous and acquired antibiotic resistance.*

■ **Genes, the Genome, and Disease** New Scientist, 17 Feb. 2001, (Inside Science). *Understanding the human genome: producing genome maps, the role of introns in gene regulation, and the future of genomic research.*

■ **Made to Measure Drugs** Biol. Sci. Rev., 14(4) April 2002, pp. 34-36. *The technical and ethical issues associated with the use of HGP information for the design of new drugs for individuals.*

■ **Genetic Screening - Controlling the Future** Biol. Sci. Rev., 12 (4) March 2000, pp. 36-38. *The techniques, applications, and ethical questions posed by genetic screening.*

■ **First Gene Therapy Approved** New Scientist, 29 November 2003, p. 13. *For the first time, a gene therapy based treatment has been given the go-ahead by regulatory authorities. The treatment consists of using an adenoviral vector to insert a p53 gene, coding for a protein that triggers cell suicide and attacks tumours.*

■ **Genes Can Come True** New Scientist, 30 Nov. 2002, pp. 30-33. *An overview of the current state of gene therapy, and a note about future directions.*

■ **What is a Stem Cell?** Biol. Sci. Rev., 16(2) November 2003, pp. 21-23. *An excellent account of the nature and uses of stem cell technology.*

■ **Tissue Engineering** Biol. Sci. Rev., 15(2) November 2002, pp. 17-19. *The technology and applications of growing tissue implants.*

■ **HIV Focus** New Scientist, 8 Feb. 2003, pp. 33-44. *A special issue covering HIV research, including vaccine development, and the new trend towards the use of protective microbiocides.*

■ **Genetic Vaccines** Scientific American, July 1999, pp. 34-41. *This excellent article includes a description of how the vaccines work and a table of specific diseases treatable by this method.*

■ **Defensive Eating** Scientific American, May 2005, pp. 13-14. *Food vaccines developed as pills.*

■ **Preparing for Battle** Scientific American, Feb. 2001, pp. 68-69. *Preparation and mode of action of the influenza vaccine. Includes discussion of the problems associated with the changing virus.*

■ **The Power to Divide** National Geographic, 208(1) July 2005. *A series of cases on different illnesses where stem cell therapy or therapeutic cloning has worked remarkably well. This account also outlines some of the ethical debates and funding issues in stem cell research.*

TEACHER'S REFERENCE

■ **New Medicines for the Developing World** Biol. Sci. Rev. 14 (1) Sept. 2001, pp. 22-26. *The politics of treating disease in the developing world: why is there little incentive to develop programmes to prevent and treat some diseases?*

■ **The Search for Blood Substitutes** Scientific American, February 1998, pp. 60-65. *Blood substitutes could be the best way to prevent the transmission of infection during transfusion.*

■ **The Promise of Tissue Engineering** Scientific American, April 1999, pp. 37-65. *An excellent series of four articles examining the current techniques and applications of this new technology.*

■ **The Stem Cell Challenge** Scientific American, June 2004, pp. 60-67. *Many technical and ethical hurdles must be overcome before stem cell technology can be widely adopted. This account discusses both the techniques and possibilities.*

■ **The Business of the Human Genome** Scientific American, July 2000, pp. 38-57. *An account of the HGP: who is involved, how the information will be used, and where the research will progress from here.*

■ **Edible Vaccines** Scientific American, Sept. 2000, pp. 48-53. *Vaccines in food may be the way of future immunisation programmes.*

■ **Designing a Dilemma** New Scientist, 11 December 1999, pp. 18-19. *A short, but useful account of preimplantation and prenatal tests.*

Internet

See pages 4-5 for details of how to access **Bio Links** from our web site: **www.thebiozone.com** From Bio Links, access sites under the topics:

HEALTH & DISEASE: • CDC disease links • WHO/OMS: health topics > **Prevention and Treatment:** • Antibiotic resistance • Antimicrobial agents • How severe is antibiotic resistance? • Inducible defenses against pathogens • Monoclonal antibodies • Monoclonal antibody technology; the basics • Resistance to antibiotics

Also see the sites listed under the subtopics Infectious diseases and Non-infectious Diseases

Presentation MEDIA to support this topic:

Health & Disease CD-ROM:
• **Set 1: The Nature of Disease**
• **Set 3: Non-Infectious Disease**

Prenatal Diagnosis of Disease

Technological advances in recent decades have enabled greater control over conception, gestation, and birth. There are now a number of commonly used prenatal (before birth) diagnostic tests that can be used to investigate foetal health and development, and test for genetic abnormalities. Prenatal diagnoses vary a lot in terms of how invasive they are to the pregnancy and how much information they provide. Tests of the α-fetoprotein levels in the mother's blood serum can indicate **Down syndrome** (low α-fetoprotein) or **neural tube defects** (high α-fetoprotein)

without risk to the foetus. Other prenatal procedures (e.g. **ultrasound**) carry a low risk and have become almost routine in some societies. **Amniocentesis** and **chorionic villus sampling** present a greater risk to both the mother and foetus and are usually reserved for the detection of chromosomal abnormalities in high risk pregnancies. All prenatal diagnostic procedures should involve supportive and accurate counselling regarding the benefits and risks of the procedure, and the choices available should the pregnancy prove to be abnormal.

Candidates for Diagnosis

Before costly and potentially high-risk prenatal tests involving chromosome analysis are carried out, there must be some clinical indication of a potential problem with either of the parents or with the pregnancy. Some **clinical indications** for chromosomal analysis are:

- Family history of inherited genetic disorders or malformities.

- History of infertility, miscarriage, stillbirth, or early neonatal death.

- First pregnancy at an older age or maternal age over 38.

Genetic counselling

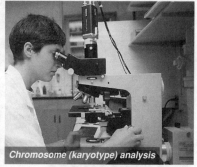
Chromosome (karyotype) analysis

Simple prenatal diagnoses (e.g. ultrasound, pictured opposite) are routinely performed in order to reassure parents that a pregnancy is normal, to check foetal growth, or to determine gender. More complex and higher risk prenatal tests involving chromosomal analysis (below and photo, above right) are not routinely performed. **Genetic counselling** (photo above, left) involves advising a patient of their risks and options and is usual practice where such tests are indicated. See the table left listing the clinical indications for chromosome analysis.

Amniocentesis

Performed at: 14-16 weeks into the pregnancy. The amniotic fluid (which naturally contains some foetal cells) is centrifuged, and the cells are cultured, examined biochemically, and karyotyped.

Used for: Detection of nearly 300 chromosomal disorders, such as Down syndrome, neural tube defects (e.g. spina bifida), and inborn errors of metabolism.

Recommended: A maternal age nearing or over 40, when parents are carriers of an inherited disorder or already have a child with a chromosomal disorder.

Associated risks: Risk of miscarriage through damage to foetus or placenta. In women younger than 35, the risk of miscarriage through the procedure is greater than the risk of carrying a child with chromosomal abnormalities.

Chorionic Villus Sampling (CVS)

Performed at: 8-10 weeks gestation. Using ultrasound guidance, a narrow tube is inserted through the cervix and a sample of the foetal chorionic villi is taken from the placenta. Compared with amniocentesis, more foetal cells are obtained so analysis can be completed earlier and more quickly.

Used for: As for amniocentesis: detection of chromosomal and metabolic disorders.

Recommended: Recommendations as for amniocentesis.

Associated risks: Risk of miscarriage is higher than for amniocentesis but, if abortion is recommended, this can be performed sooner. Note that both amniocentesis and CVS rely on the ultrasound to determine the position of the foetus and placenta in the uterus.

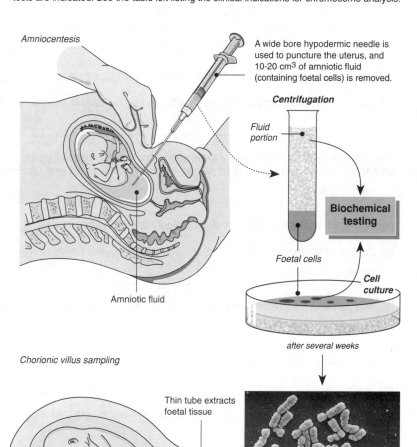

Amniocentesis

A wide bore hypodermic needle is used to puncture the uterus, and 10-20 cm³ of amniotic fluid (containing foetal cells) is removed.

Centrifugation

Fluid portion

Biochemical testing

Foetal cells

Cell culture

Amniotic fluid

after several weeks

Chorionic villus sampling

Thin tube extracts foetal tissue

after 24 hours

Karyotyping for abnormalities

© Biozone International 2006

Photocopying Prohibited

Preventing and Treating Disease

Code: RA 2

Ultrasound in Pregnancy

Ultrasound is commonly used to view the uterus and foetus during pregnancy. Scans are often performed at 18 to 20 weeks into a pregnancy, frequently as a routine procedure. They may also be performed earlier (at about 10-11 weeks) or later (after 34 weeks) if problems are indicated (e.g. severe vomiting in early pregnancy, gestational diabetes, or indications that the foetus is not growing normally). Ultrasound is used for the diagnosis of multiple pregnancies (twins) and gross foetal abnormalities (e.g. trisomy). It is also used to determine foetal age and growth, gender, conception date, and placental position. Such information aids pregnancy management. Ultrasound is apparently safe, but the risks associated with frequent scans are unknown.

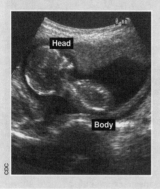

The reflected sound waves give a visual echo of the foetus inside the uterus.

In this 4 month old foetus, the general shape of the body and limbs can be discerned. The operator magnifies regions of interest in order to take more accurate measurements.

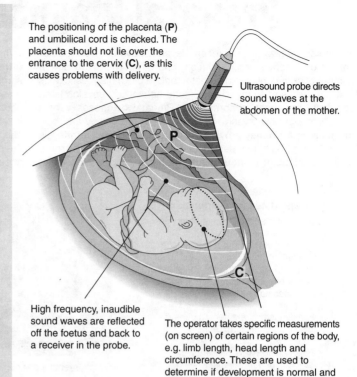

The positioning of the placenta (**P**) and umbilical cord is checked. The placenta should not lie over the entrance to the cervix (**C**), as this causes problems with delivery.

Ultrasound probe directs sound waves at the abdomen of the mother.

High frequency, inaudible sound waves are reflected off the foetus and back to a receiver in the probe.

The operator takes specific measurements (on screen) of certain regions of the body, e.g. limb length, head length and circumference. These are used to determine if development is normal and growth is within the expected range.

1. (a) Explain the medical reasons why an ultrasound scan might be used to examine a foetus:

_____

_____

(b) Name one other feature that may be detected with ultrasound: _____

(c) Explain why ultrasound scans are usually performed later in pregnancy (20 weeks):

_____

2. Chorionic villus sampling (CVS), if performed very early in pregnancy (at 5-7 weeks) may cause limb abnormalities, probably via upsetting critical sites of foetal blood flow. Suggest why CVS might be performed at such an early stage:

_____

3. Name one chromosomal disorder detectable through amniocentesis: _____

4. (a) Explain why amniocentesis is not usually recommended for women younger than 35:

_____

(b) Suggest when amniocentesis might be recommended for younger women, in spite of the risk:

_____

5. State two clinical indications for needing a prenatal test involving chromosome analysis:

(a) _____ (b) _____

6. Suggest why a history of infertility or miscarriage may indicate that a parent is carrying an inherited genetic disorder:

_____

7. Describe some of the ethical concerns of the following information gained through prenatal diagnoses:

(a) Gender determination: _____

_____

(b) Termination of a viable pregnancy: _____

_____

Postnatal Testing

There are a number of genetically inherited metabolic disorders in humans that involve interruption of metabolic pathways. Most are very rare with incidence rates of one in millions. However, some are common enough to warrant testing of all newborn babies (five days after birth). The baby's blood sample is taken by a nurse at the hospital, or a midwife or doctor at home, and blotted onto an absorbent card (see below). The sample is sent away for tests that could save the baby's life, or enable prevention

of serious physical or mental problems. Most babies born in Britain are normal. A very few have rare, but serious disorders that are caused by a defective gene that gives rise to a defective protein. This protein is usually an enzyme that is unable to carry out its vital step in a metabolic pathway. Newborn blood tests are carried out at special testing centres in each country. In the UK (below), these laboratories currently test for three disorders, two of which are caused by recessive genes on autosomes.

Metabolic Disorders Tested in Newborns

Congenital Hypothyroidism (sporadic)

Caused by: Not enough normal thyroid gland.
Leads to: Slowed growth and mental development.
Probability: 1 in **3400** newborn babies

Galactosaemia (autosomal recessive)

Caused by: An enzyme defect prevents normal use of galactose (part of milk sugar, lactose).
Leads to: Jaundice, cataracts, and severe illness.
Probability: 1 in **70 000** newborn babies

Phenylketonuria (PKU) (autosomal recessive)

Caused by: A faulty gene means an enzyme is missing from the liver. Without this enzyme, the essential amino acid phenylalanine rises to harmful levels.
Leads to: Brain damage.
Probability: 1 in **6500** newborn babies

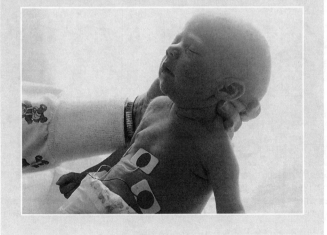

Newborn Baby Blood Test

The card below shows the front of the blood test collecting paper (a kind of blotting paper). Blood is obtained from a heel prick from the baby's foot on the 5th day after birth and applied to each of the three circles at the bottom of the card.

PKU BLOOD TEST
PLEASE PRINT USING A BALLPOINT PEN

Name _____
Address and Full Post Code _____

District Health Board _____
Place of Birth _____
G.P. Name _____
Address _____
_____
Date of Birth _____ Sex _____
Date of First Milk Feed _____

Mother's DOB _____
Type of Feeding – Bottle ☐   Breast ☐   Other ☐
Tick if Baby is Premature ☐ On Antibiotics ☐ In Hospital ☐
Date Specimen Taken _____
Name of person taking the specimen _____

FILL ALL CIRCLES THROUGH TO THE BACK WITH BLOOD

◯ ◯ ◯ ◯

Please ensure that ALL information requested on the card is filled in correctly

Blood is applied here, filling each of the 4 circles

Results of the test
- The vast majority of results are negative for all three of the conditions described (above left).
- The results of the test should be available within a few days of the test being taken.
- If a test is positive, a paediatrician is consulted to discuss the results and treatment.

Repeat tests
It is necessary to collect a second blood sample if:
- There was not enough blood in the first sample.
- The sample was damaged or did not reach the lab.
- The result was borderline (inconclusive).

1. Explain what is meant by a **metabolic disorder**: _____
_____

2. Explain briefly the purpose of the **newborn baby blood test**: _____
_____

3. Suggest why the blood samples are not taken until the 5th day after birth: _____
_____

4. Giving an example, define the term **congenital**: _____

Code: RA 1

Genetic Counselling

Genetic counselling is an analysis of the risk of producing offspring with known gene defects within a family. Counsellors identify families at risk, investigate the problem present in the family, interpret information about the disorder, analyse inheritance patterns and risks of recurrence, and review available options with the family. Increasingly, there are DNA tests for the identification of specific defective genes. People usually consider genetic counselling if they have a family history of a genetic disorder, or if a routine prenatal screening test yields an unexpected result. While screening for many genetic disorders is now recommended, the use of presymptomatic tests for adult-onset disorders, such as Alzheimer's, is still controversial.

Autosomal Recessive Conditions

Common inherited disorders caused by recessive alleles on autosomes. Recessive conditions are evident only in homozygous recessive genotypes

Cystic fibrosis: Malfunction of the pancreas and other glands; thick mucus leads to pneumonia and emphysema. Death usually occurs in childhood. CF is the most frequent lethal genetic disorder in childhood (about 1 case in 3700 live births).

Maple syrup urine disease: Mental and physical retardation produced by a block in amino acid metabolism. Isoleucine in the urine produces the characteristic odour.

Tay-Sachs disease: A lipid storage disease which causes progressive developmental paralysis, mental deterioration, and blindness. Death usually occurs by three years of age.

Autosomal Dominant Conditions

Inherited disorders caused by dominant alleles on autosomes. Dominant conditions are evident both in heterozygotes and in homozygous dominant individuals

Huntington disease: Involuntary movements of the face and limbs with later general mental deterioration. The beginning of symptoms is highly variable, but occurs usually between 30 to 40 years of age.

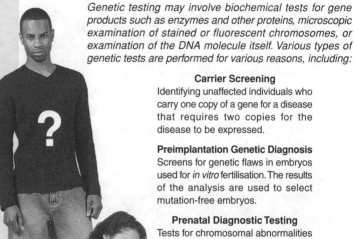

Genetic testing may involve biochemical tests for gene products such as enzymes and other proteins, microscopic examination of stained or fluorescent chromosomes, or examination of the DNA molecule itself. Various types of genetic tests are performed for various reasons, including:

Carrier Screening
Identifying unaffected individuals who carry one copy of a gene for a disease that requires two copies for the disease to be expressed.

Preimplantation Genetic Diagnosis
Screens for genetic flaws in embryos used for *in vitro* fertilisation. The results of the analysis are used to select mutation-free embryos.

Prenatal Diagnostic Testing
Tests for chromosomal abnormalities such as Down syndrome.

Newborn Screening
Newborn babies are screened for a variety of enzyme-based disorders.

Presymptomatic Testing
Testing before symptoms are apparent is important for estimating the risk of developing adult-onset disorders, including Huntington's, cancers, and Alzheimer's disease.

Auditory test

About half of the cases of childhood deafness are the result of an autosomal recessive disorder. Early identification of the problem prepares families and allows early appropriate treatment.

Genetic counselling provides information to families who have members with birth defects or genetic disorders, and to families who may be at risk for a variety of inherited conditions.

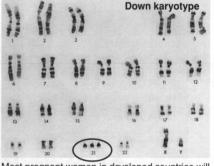

Down karyotype

Cytogenetics Dept., Waikato Hospital

Most pregnant women in developed countries will have a prenatal test to detect chromosomal abnormalities such as Down syndrome and developmental anomalies such as neural defects.

1. Outline the benefits of **carrier screening** to a couple with a family history of a genetic disorder:

_____

_____

2. (a) Suggest why Huntington disease persists in the human population when it is caused by a lethal, dominant allele:

_____

_____

(b) Explain how presymptomatic genetic testing could change this: _____

_____

_____

Diagnosing Medical Problems

The proper and prompt treatment of disease requires accurate and rapid diagnosis. Some diagnostic techniques, such as CT and MRI scans, are very sophisticated, while others (e.g. blood tests) are much less complicated. Examples are given below.

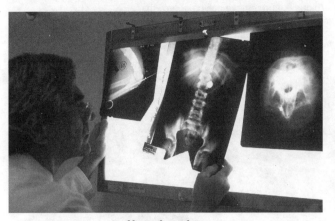

X-ray imaging

X-rays are a form of electromagnetic radiation that can pass through tissues and expose photographic film. The X-rays are absorbed by dense body tissues (e.g. bone) which appear as white areas, but they pass easily through less dense tissues (e.g. muscle), which appear dark. X-rays are used to identify fractures or abnormalities in bone. X-ray technology is also used in conjunction with computer imaging techniques (see below).

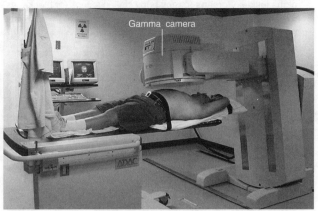

Gamma camera

Radionuclide scanning

Radionuclide scanning involves introducing a radioactive substance (the radionuclide) into the body, where it is taken up in different amounts by different tissues (e.g. radioactive iodine is taken up preferentially by the thyroid). The radiation emitted by the tissues that take up the radionuclide is detected by a gamma camera. Radionuclide scanning provides better detail of function than other techniques, but gives less anatomical detail.

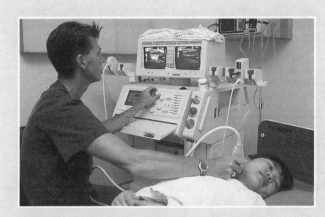

Diagnostic uses of ultrasound

Ultrasound is a diagnostic tool used to visualise internal structures without surgery or X-rays. Ultrasound imaging is based on the fact that tissues of different densities reflect sound waves differently. Sound waves are directed towards a structure (e.g. uterus, heart, kidney, liver) and the reflected sound waves are recorded. An image of the internal structures is analysed by computer and displayed on a screen.

Echocardiography uses ultrasound to investigate heart disorders such as congenital heart disease and valve disorders. The liver and other abdominal organs can also be viewed with ultrasound for diagnosis of disorders such as cirrhosis, cysts, blockages, and tumours. Ultrasound scans of the uterus are commonly used during pregnancy to indicate placental position and aspects of foetal growth and development. This information aids better pregnancy management.

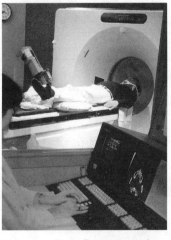

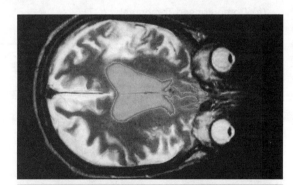

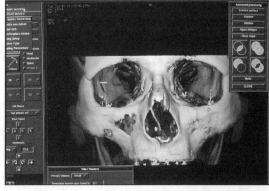

Computer imaging techniques

Computers are used extensively to examine the soft tissues of the body for diagnostic purposes. The photos directly above show **magnetic resonance imaging** (MRI), which uses computer analysis of high frequency radio waves to map out variations in tissue density, especially of the central nervous system (above, far right). In **computerised tomography** (CT) scans, a series of X-rays is made through an organ and the picture from each X-ray slice is reconstructed (using computer software) into a 3-D image (e.g. the skull, right). Such images can be used to detect abnormalities such as tumours.

Preventing and Treating Disease

Code: A 2

Endoscopy

An **endoscope** is an illuminated tube comprising fibre-optic cables with lenses attached. Endoscopy can be used for a visual inspection of the inside of organs (or any body cavity) to look for blockages or damage. Endoscopes can also be fitted with devices to remove foreign objects, temporarily stop bleeding, remove tissue samples (biopsy), and remove polyps or growths.

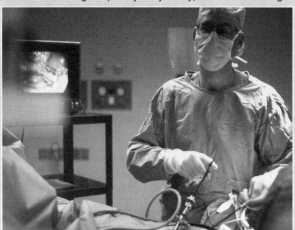

Laparoscopy is the endoscopic examination of the organs in the abdominal cavity, and is used during simple surgical operations (e.g. tubal ligation). Endoscopic examination of the stomach is called gastroscopy.

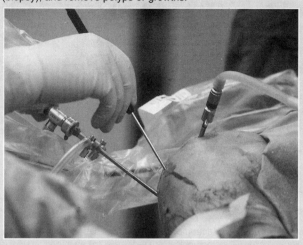

Arthroscopy is used for inspecting joints, usually knee joints (above), while the patient is under a general anaesthetic. Using very small incisions, damaged cartilage can be removed from the joint using other instruments.

Biosensors

Biosensors are electronic monitoring devices that use biological material to detect the presence or concentration of a particular substance. Because of their specificity and sensitivity, enzymes are ideally suited for use in biosensors. The example below illustrates how the enzyme **glucose oxidase** is used to detect blood sugar level in diabetics.

The enzyme, *glucose oxidase* is immobilised in a semi-conducting silicon chip. It catalyses the conversion of glucose (from the blood sample) to gluconic acid.

Hydrogen ions from the gluconic acid cause a movement of electrons in the silicon which is detected by a transducer. The strength of the electric current is directly proportional to the blood glucose concentration.

Results are shown on a liquid crystal display.

Plastic sleeve — Membrane permeable to glucose — **Biological recognition layer** — **Transducer** — **Amplifier** — **932**

The signal is amplified

1. Describe the basic principle of the scanning technology behind each of the following computer imaging techniques:

   (a) Computerised Tomography (CT): _____

   _____

   (b) Magnetic Resonance Imaging (MRI): _____

   _____

2. Describe the benefits of using computer imaging techniques such as MRI or CT: _____

   _____

3. Explain how radionuclide scanning differs from X-rays: _____

   _____

4. Describe the benefits of endoscope technology over conventional open surgery: _____

   _____

5. Describe the basic principle of a biosensor: _____

   _____

   _____

   _____

A Balanced Diet

Nutrients are required for metabolism, tissue growth and repair, and as an energy source. Good nutrition (provided by a **balanced diet**) is recognised as a key factor in good health. Conversely poor nutrition (malnutrition) may cause ill-health or **deficiency diseases**. A diet refers to the quantity and nature of the food eaten. While not all foods contain all the representative nutrients, we can obtain the required balance of different nutrients by eating a wide variety of foods. In a recent overhaul of previous dietary recommendations, the health benefits of monounsaturated fats (such as olive and canola oils), fish oils, and whole grains have

been recognised, and people are being urged to reduce their consumption of highly processed foods and saturated (rather than total) fat. Those on diets that restrict certain food groups (e.g. vegans) must take care to balance their intake of foods to ensure an adequate supply of protein and other nutrients (e.g. iron and B vitamins). **Reference Nutrient Intakes** (RNIs) in the UK (overleaf), and their equivalents in other countries, provide nutritional guidelines for different sectors of the population. They help to define the limits of adequate nutrient intake for most people, although not necessarily those with special needs.

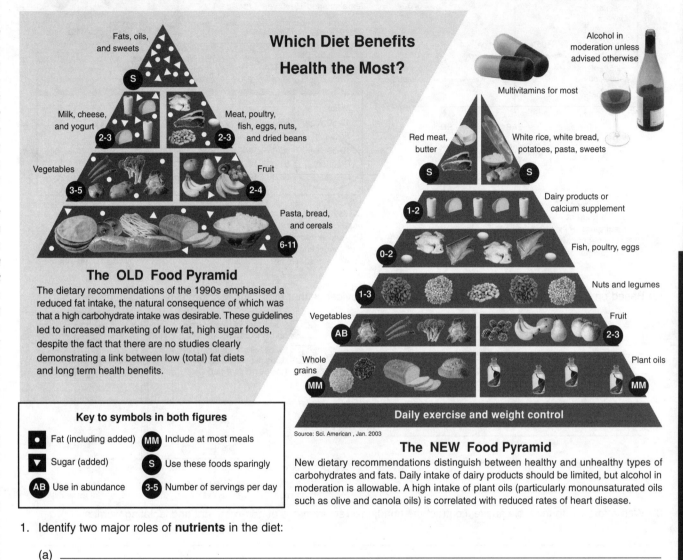

Which Diet Benefits Health the Most?

The OLD Food Pyramid

The dietary recommendations of the 1990s emphasised a reduced fat intake, the natural consequence of which was that a high carbohydrate intake was desirable. These guidelines led to increased marketing of low fat, high sugar foods, despite the fact that there are no studies clearly demonstrating a link between low (total) fat diets and long term health benefits.

Source: Sci. American , Jan. 2003

The NEW Food Pyramid

New dietary recommendations distinguish between healthy and unhealthy types of carbohydrates and fats. Daily intake of dairy products should be limited, but alcohol in moderation is allowable. A high intake of plant oils (particularly monounsaturated oils such as olive and canola oils) is correlated with reduced rates of heart disease.

Key to symbols in both figures

- ◼ Fat (including added)
- ▼ Sugar (added)
- AB Use in abundance
- MM Include at most meals
- S Use these foods sparingly
- 3-5 Number of servings per day

Preventing and Treating Disease

1. Identify two major roles of **nutrients** in the diet:

    (a) _____

    (b) _____

2. (a) Compare the two food pyramids (above) and discuss how they differ in their recommendations for good nutrition:

    _____

    _____

    _____

    _____

    _____

    _____

    _____

    _____

Nutritional Guidelines in the UK

In the UK, Dietary Reference Values (**DRVs**) provide guidelines for nutrient and energy intake for particular groups of the population. In this scheme, it is assumed that the nutritional requirements of the population are represented by a normal, bell-shaped, curve (below). DRVs collectively encompass RNIs, LRNIs, and EARs. In the UK, DRVs have replaced Recommended Daily Amounts (RDAs), which are still used in the USA and elsewhere, and provide similar guidelines for nutrition, although based on slightly different criteria.

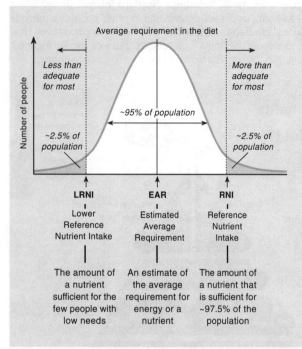

LRNI
Lower Reference Nutrient Intake

The amount of a nutrient sufficient for the few people with low needs

EAR
Estimated Average Requirement

An estimate of the average requirement for energy or a nutrient

RNI
Reference Nutrient Intake

The amount of a nutrient that is sufficient for ~97.5% of the population

Table 1 (below): Estimated Average Requirements (EAR) for energy, and Reference Nutrient Intakes (RNIs) for selected nutrients, for UK males and females aged 19-50 years (per day).

Source: Dept of Health. Dietary Reference Values for Food Energy and Nutrients for the UK, 1991.

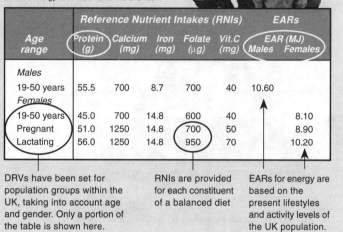

Age range	Reference Nutrient Intakes (RNIs)					EARs	
	Protein (g)	Calcium (mg)	Iron (mg)	Folate (µg)	Vit.C (mg)	EAR (MJ) Males	Females
Males							
19-50 years	55.5	700	8.7	700	40	10.60	
Females							
19-50 years	45.0	700	14.8	600	40		8.10
Pregnant	51.0	1250	14.8	700	50		8.90
Lactating	56.0	1250	14.8	950	70		10.20

DRVs have been set for population groups within the UK, taking into account age and gender. Only a portion of the table is shown here.

RNIs are provided for each constituent of a balanced diet

EARs for energy are based on the present lifestyles and activity levels of the UK population.

(b) Based on the information on the graph (right), state the evidence that might support the revised recommendations:

_____

_____

_____

_____

_____

_____

_____

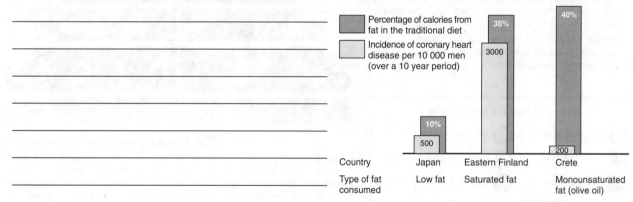

■ Percentage of calories from fat in the traditional diet

□ Incidence of coronary heart disease per 10 000 men (over a 10 year period)

Country	Japan	Eastern Finland	Crete
Type of fat consumed	Low fat	Saturated fat	Monounsaturated fat (olive oil)

3. With reference to the table above, contrast the nutritional requirements of non-pregnant and lactating women:

_____

_____

4. Suggest why recommendations (such as DRVs), which are based on the nutritional needs of most people in the population, might be preferable to those (such as RDAs) which try to encompass the needs of the whole population:

_____

_____

_____

5. Suggest how DRVs (or their equivalents) can be applied in each of the following situations:

(a) Dietary planning and assessment: _____

_____

(b) Food labelling and consumer information: _____

_____

The Health Benefits of Exercise

Regular exercise helps protect against a range of health problems, improves mood, and assists in managing stress. Exercise promotes health by improving the rate of blood flow back to the heart (**venous return**). This is achieved by strengthening all types of muscle and by increasing the efficiency of the heart. During exercise blood flow to different parts of the body changes in order to cope with the extra demands of the muscles, the heart and the lungs. Over time, regular exercise leads to greater **endurance**, and improves the body's ability to respond to everyday demands of physical activity.

Risk	Specific Health Benefits of Exercise
Heart disease and stroke	Strengthens heart muscle, lowers blood pressure, improves blood flow, and increases the heart's working capacity.
Obesity and high blood pressure	Exercise reduces body fat by building or preserving muscle mass and improving the body's ability to use calories. Combined with proper nutrition, exercise controls weight and prevents obesity, which is associated with many diseases, including high blood pressure (hypertension).
Non-insulin dependent diabetes	Weight loss associated with exercise prevents and controls adult onset diabetes mellitus.
Osteoporosis	Regular weight bearing exercise promotes bone formation and prevents age-related bone loss.
Back pain	Helps to prevent back pain by increasing muscle strength and endurance, and improving flexibility and posture.
Cancers	Exercise lowers the risk of breast and colon cancers.

Regular, moderate exercise promotes psychological well-being, improves immune function, reduces muscular and mental tension, and increases concentration and energy levels.

Strength and resistance exercises, often with machines or weights, are an important component of physiotherapy for people recovering from trauma or illness.

Exercise is a social activity for many, providing a reason for regular social contact. Exercise also increases self-esteem and confidence, and reduces feelings of anxiety and depression

A basic level of fitness is essential for maintaining muscular strength and flexibility into old age. Without it, people lose the ability to do everyday activities such as housework or lifting.

1. (a) Explain how the body increases the rate of blood flow during exercise: _____

_____

(b) Describe the physiological effects of this when exercise is performed on a regular basis: _____

_____

(c) Explain how these changes benefit health in the long term: _____

_____

_____

_____

Code: DA 2

Endurance refers to the ability of the muscles and the cardiovascular and respiratory systems to carry out exercise. Muscular endurance allows sprinters to run fast for a short time or body builders and weight lifters to lift an immense weight and hold it for a few seconds. Cardiovascular and respiratory endurance refer to the body as a whole: the ability to endure a high level of activity over a prolonged period. This type of endurance is seen in marathon runners, and long distance swimmers and cyclists. Different sports ("short burst sports" compared with endurance type sports) require different training methods and the physiologies (muscle bulk and cardiovascular fitness) of the athletes can be quite different.

The human heart and circulatory system make a number of adjustments in response to aerobic or endurance training. These include:

- **Heart size**: Increases. The left ventricle wall becomes thicker and its chamber bigger.

- **Heart rate**: Heart rate (at rest and during exercise) decreases markedly from non-trained people.

- **Recovery**: Recovery after exercise (of breathing and heart rate) is faster in trained athletes.

- **Stroke volume**: The volume of blood pumped with each heart beat increases with endurance training.

- **Blood volume**: Endurance training increases blood volume (the amount of blood in the body).

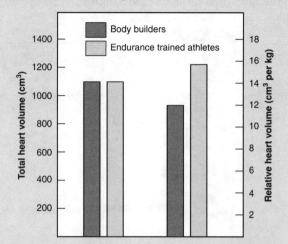

Difference in heart size of highly trained body builders and endurance athletes. Total heart volume is compared to heart volume as related to body weight. Average weights as follows: Body builders = 90.1 kg. Endurance athletes = 68.7 kg.

2. The table (right) provides data for the **rate** of blood flow to various parts of the body at rest and during strenuous exercise. **Calculate** the **percentage** of the total blood flow that each organ or tissue receives under each regime of activity.

3. (a) State approximately how many times the total rate of blood flow increases between rest and exercise:

_____

(b) Explain why the increase is needed:

_____

_____

_____

_____

Organ or tissue	At rest		Strenuous exercise	
	cm³ min⁻¹	% of total	cm³ min⁻¹	% of total
Brain	700	14	750	4.2
Heart	200		750	
Lung tissue	100		200	
Kidneys	1100		600	
Liver	1350		600	
Skeletal muscles	750		12 500	
Bone	250		250	
Skin	300		1900	
Thyroid gland	50		50	
Adrenal glands	25		25	
Other tissue	175		175	
TOTAL	5000	**100**	17 800	**100**

4. Identify the organs or tissues that show the most change in the rate of blood flow with exercise and explain why:

_____

_____

5. Suggest why heart size increases with cardiovascular endurance activity: _____

_____

6. Heart stroke volume increases with endurance training. Explain how this increases the efficiency of the heart as a pump:

_____

_____

The Control of Infectious Disease

Many factors can influence the spread of disease, including the social climate, diet, general health, and access to medical care. Human intervention and modification of behaviour can reduce the transmission rate of some diseases and inhibit their spread. Examples include the use of personal physical barriers, such as condoms, to prevent sexually transmitted infections (STIs), and the use of **quarantine** to ensure that potential carriers of disease are isolated until incubation periods have elapsed. Cleaning up the environment also lowers the incidence of disease by reducing the likelihood that pathogens or their vectors will survive. The effective control of infectious disease depends on knowing the origin of the outbreak (its natural reservoir), its mode of transmission within the population, and the methods that can be feasibly employed to contain it. Diseases are often classified according to how they behave in a given population. Any disease that spreads from one host to another, either directly or indirectly, is said to be a **communicable disease**. Those that are easily spread from one person to another, such as chicken pox or measles, are said to be **contagious**. Such diseases are a threat to **public health** and many must be notified to health authorities. **Noncommunicable diseases** are not spread from one host to another and pose less of a threat to public health. A disease that occurs only occasionally and is usually restricted in its spread is called a **sporadic disease**.

Methods for controlling the spread of disease

Transmission of disease can be prevented or reduced by adopting 'safe' behaviours. Examples include using condoms to reduce the spread of STIs, isolation of people with a specific illness (such as SARS), or establishing quarantine procedures for people who may be infected, but are not yet ill.

The development of effective sanitation, sewage treatment, and treatment of drinking water has virtually eliminated dangerous waterborne diseases from developed countries. These practices disrupt the normal infection cycle of pathogens such as cholera and giardia.

Appropriate personal hygiene practices reduce the risk of infection and transmission. Soap may not destroy the pathogens but washing will dilute and remove them from the skin. Although popular, antibacterial soaps encourage development of strains resistant to antimicrobial agents.

The environment can be made less suitable for the growth and transmission of pathogens. For example, spraying drainage ditches and draining swamps eliminates breeding habitats for mosquitoes carrying diseases such as malaria and dengue fever.

Immunisation schedules form part of public health programmes. If most of the population is immune, 'herd immunity' limits outbreaks to sporadic cases. In such populations there are too few susceptible individuals to support the spread of an epidemic.

Disinfectants and sterilisation techniques, such as autoclaving, destroy pathogenic microbes before they have the opportunity to infect. The use of these techniques in medicine has significantly reduced post operative infections and associated deaths.

Preventing and Treating Disease

1. Distinguish between contagious and non-communicable diseases, providing an example of each:

_____

_____

2. (a) Explain the difference between **isolation** and **quarantine**: _____

_____

_____

_____

Code: RA 2

(b) Using the example of SARS, explain how isolation and quarantine operate to prevent the spread of disease:

_____

_____

3. Explain how the use of condoms reduces the spread of the human immunodeficiency virus (HIV) that causes AIDS:

_____

_____

4. Explain how the drainage of stagnant water in tropical regions may reduce the incidence of malaria in those countries:

_____

_____

5. Describe how each of the following methods is used to control the **growth** of disease-causing microbes:

(a) Disinfectants: _____

_____

(b) Antiseptics: _____

_____

(c) Heat: _____

_____

(d) Ionising radiation (gamma rays): _____

_____

(e) Desiccation: _____

_____

(f) Cold: _____

6. The **Human Genome Project** (HGP) has acheived its aim of sequencing the entire human genome, and much of the research since has focussed on determining the various roles of the (expressed) gene products. It is hoped that a more complete understanding the human genome will revolutionise the treatment and prevention of disease. Briefly discuss how the HGP will facilitate:

(a) Diagnosis of disease: _____

_____

_____

(b) Treatment of disease: _____

_____

_____

7. The first measles vaccine was introduced to Britain in 1964. However, in 1993 there were 9000 cases of measles notified to the health authorities in England and Wales.

(a) Suggest why measles has not been eliminated in Britain: _____

_____

(b) Explain how vaccination interrupts the transmission of measles within a population: _____

_____

_____

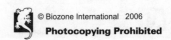

Antimicrobial Drugs

Antimicrobial drugs include synthetic (manufactured) **drugs** as well as drugs produced by bacteria and fungi, called **antibiotics**. Antibiotics are produced naturally by these microorganisms as a means of inhibiting competing microbes around them (a form of antibiosis, hence the name antibiotic). The first antibiotic, called penicillin, was discovered in 1928 by Alexander Fleming. Since then, similar inhibitory reactions between colonies growing on solid media have been commonly observed. Antibiotics are actually rather easy to discover, but few of them are of medical or commercial value. Many antibiotics are toxic to humans or lack any advantage over those already in use. More than half of our antibiotics are produced by species of filamentous bacteria that commonly inhabit the soil, called *Streptomyces*. A few antibiotics are produced by bacteria of the genus *Bacillus*. Others are produced by moulds, mostly of the genera *Cephalosporium* and *Penicillium*. Antimicrobial drugs are used in **chemotherapy** programmes to treat infectious diseases. Like disinfectants, these chemicals interfere with the growth

of microorganisms (see diagram below). They may either kill microbes directly (**bactericidal**) or prevent them from growing (**bacteriostatic**). To be effective, they must often act inside the host, so their effect on the host's cells and tissues is important. The ideal antimicrobial drug has **selective toxicity**, killing the pathogen without damaging the host. Some antimicrobial drugs have a narrow **spectrum of activity**, and affect only a limited number of microbial types. Others are **broad-spectrum drugs** and affect a large number of microbial species (see the table below). When the identity of a pathogen is not known, a broad-spectrum drug may be prescribed in order to save valuable time. There is a disadvantage with this, because broad spectrum drugs target not just the pathogen, but much of the host's normal microflora also. The normal microbial community usually controls the growth of pathogens and other microbes by competing with them. By selectively removing them with drugs, certain microbes in the community that do not normally cause problems, may flourish and become **opportunistic pathogens**.

How Antimicrobial Drugs Work

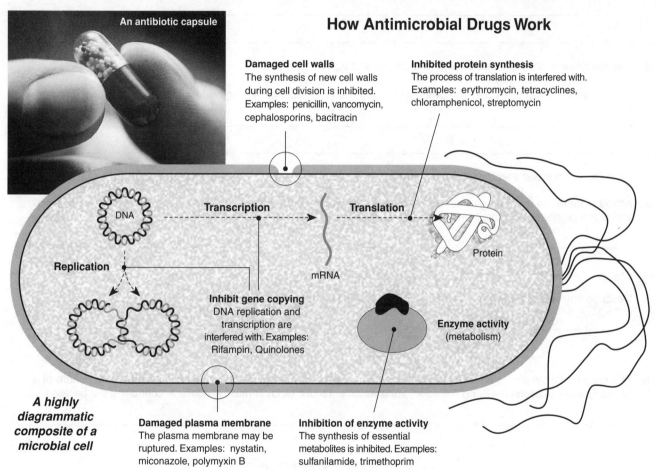

An antibiotic capsule

Damaged cell walls
The synthesis of new cell walls during cell division is inhibited. Examples: penicillin, vancomycin, cephalosporins, bacitracin

Inhibited protein synthesis
The process of translation is interfered with. Examples: erythromycin, tetracyclines, chloramphenicol, streptomycin

Transcription   Translation
DNA
Protein
mRNA
Replication

Inhibit gene copying
DNA replication and transcription are interfered with. Examples: Rifampin, Quinolones

Enzyme activity
(metabolism)

A highly diagrammatic composite of a microbial cell

Damaged plasma membrane
The plasma membrane may be ruptured. Examples: nystatin, miconazole, polymyxin B

Inhibition of enzyme activity
The synthesis of essential metabolites is inhibited. Examples: sulfanilamide, trimethoprim

Preventing and Treating Disease

Spectrum of antimicrobial activity of a number of chemotherapeutic drugs

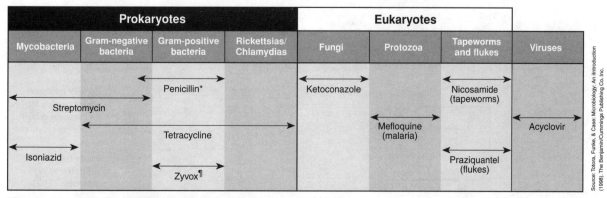

Prokaryotes				Eukaryotes			
Mycobacteria	Gram-negative bacteria	Gram-positive bacteria	Rickettsias/ Chlamydias	Fungi	Protozoa	Tapeworms and flukes	Viruses
		Penicillin* →		Ketoconazole		Nicosamide (tapeworms)	
← Streptomycin →							
		Tetracycline			Mefloquine (malaria)		Acyclovir
← Isoniazid →						Praziquantel (flukes)	
		Zyvox¶					

Source: Totora, Funke, & Case: Microbiology: An Introduction (1998); The Benjamin/Cummings Publishing Co. Inc.

* There are some synthetic derivatives of penicillin that act effectively against gram-negative bacteria.
¶ The first new class of antibiotics to be used in 35 years.

Code: A 2

1. Discuss the requirements of an "ideal" antimicrobial drug, and explain in what way antibiotics satisfy these requirements:

_____

_____

_____

_____

2. Some bacteria have ways of tolerating treatment by antibiotics, and are termed 'superbugs'.

   (a) Explain what is meant by **antibiotic resistance** in bacteria: _____

   _____

   _____

   (b) Explain why a course of antibiotics should be finished completely, even when the symptoms of infection have gone:

   _____

   _____

3. The spectrum of activity varies for different groups of drugs.

   (a) Explain the advantages and disadvantages of using a broad-spectrum drug on an unidentified bacterial infection:

   _____

   _____

   (b) Identify two broad spectrum groups of drugs: _____

4. Although there are a few drugs that have some success in controlling viruses, antibiotics are ineffective. Explain why antibiotics do not work against viruses:

   _____

   _____

   _____

5. Describe four ways in which antimicrobial drugs kill or inhibit the growth of microbes: _____

   _____

   _____

   _____

6. The diagram below shows an experiment investigating the effectiveness of different antibiotics on a pure culture of a single species of bacteria. Giving a reason, state which antibiotic (A-D) is most effective in controlling the bacteria:

   _____

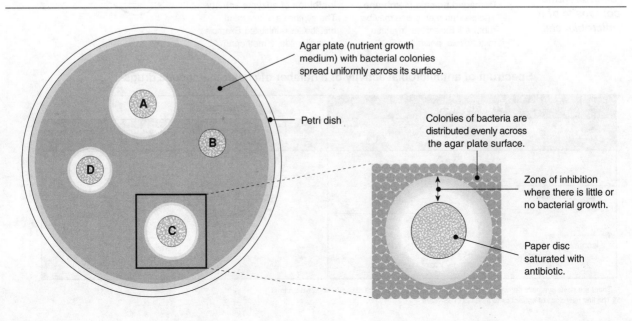

Agar plate (nutrient growth medium) with bacterial colonies spread uniformly across its surface.

Petri dish

Colonies of bacteria are distributed evenly across the agar plate surface.

Zone of inhibition where there is little or no bacterial growth.

Paper disc saturated with antibiotic.

Monoclonal Antibodies

A **monoclonal antibody** is an artificially produced antibody that binds to and inactivates only one specific protein (antigen). Monoclonal antibodies are produced in the laboratory by stimulating the production of B-lymphocytes in mice injected with the antigen. These B-lymphocytes produce an antibody against the antigen. When isolated and made to fuse with immortal tumour cells, they can be cultured indefinitely in a suitable growing medium (as shown below). Monoclonal antibodies are useful for three reasons: they are totally uniform (i.e. clones), they can be produced in very large quantities at low cost, and they are highly specific. The uses of antibodies produced by this method range from diagnostic tools, to treatments for infections and cancer, and prevention of tissue rejection in transplant patients. Many of the diagnostic tests, e.g. for some sexually transmitted or parasitic infections, previously required relatively difficult culturing or microscopic methods for diagnosis. In addition, newer diagnostic tests using monoclonal antibodies are easier to interpret and often require fewer highly trained personnel.

Making Monoclonal Antibodies

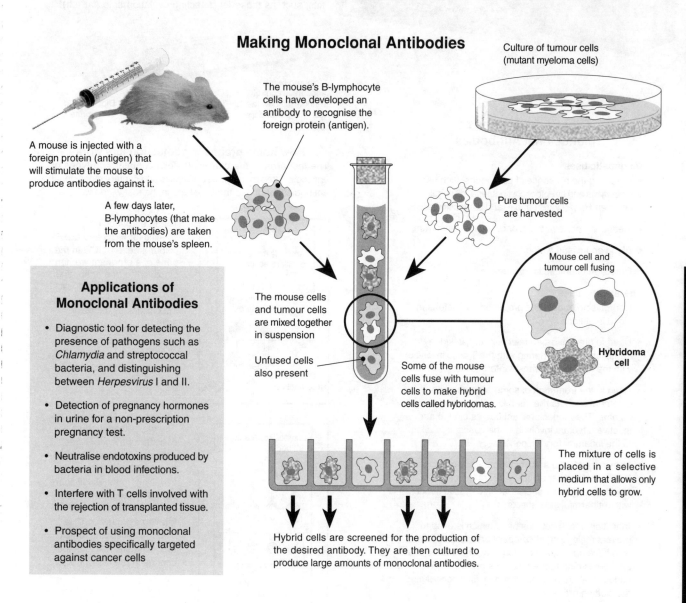

Culture of tumour cells (mutant myeloma cells)

The mouse's B-lymphocyte cells have developed an antibody to recognise the foreign protein (antigen).

A mouse is injected with a foreign protein (antigen) that will stimulate the mouse to produce antibodies against it.

A few days later, B-lymphocytes (that make the antibodies) are taken from the mouse's spleen.

Pure tumour cells are harvested

Mouse cell and tumour cell fusing

The mouse cells and tumour cells are mixed together in suspension

Unfused cells also present

Some of the mouse cells fuse with tumour cells to make hybrid cells called hybridomas.

Hybridoma cell

Applications of Monoclonal Antibodies

- Diagnostic tool for detecting the presence of pathogens such as *Chlamydia* and streptococcal bacteria, and distinguishing between *Herpesvirus* I and II.

- Detection of pregnancy hormones in urine for a non-prescription pregnancy test.

- Neutralise endotoxins produced by bacteria in blood infections.

- Interfere with T cells involved with the rejection of transplanted tissue.

- Prospect of using monoclonal antibodies specifically targeted against cancer cells

The mixture of cells is placed in a selective medium that allows only hybrid cells to grow.

Hybrid cells are screened for the production of the desired antibody. They are then cultured to produce large amounts of monoclonal antibodies.

Preventing and Treating Disease

1. Identify the mouse cells used to produce the monoclonal antibodies: _____

2. Describe the characteristic of tumour cells that allows an ongoing culture of antibody-producing lymphocytes to be made:

   _____

   _____

3. Compare the method of producing monoclonal antibodies using mice with the alternative methods now available:

   _____

   _____

   _____

   _____

Code: RA 2

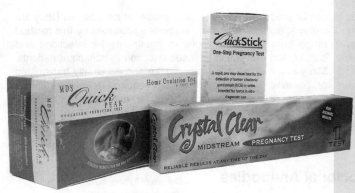

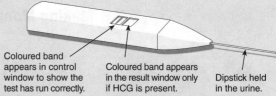

Detecting Pregnancy using Monoclonal Antibodies

When a woman becomes pregnant, a hormone called **human chorionic gonadotropin** (HCG) is released from the placenta. HCG accumulates in the bloodstream and is excreted in the urine. HCG is a glycoprotein, which means antibodies can be produced against it and used in simple test kits (below) to determine if a woman is pregnant. Monoclonal antibodies are also used in other home testing kits, such as those for detecting ovulation time (far left).

Coloured band appears in control window to show the test has run correctly.

Coloured band appears in the result window only if HCG is present.

Dipstick held in the urine.

How home pregnancy detection kits work

The test area of the dipstick (below) contains two types of antibodies: free monoclonal antibodies and capture monoclonal antibodies, bound to the substrate in the test window.

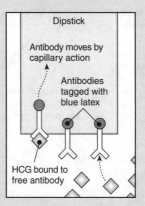

Dipstick

Antibody moves by capillary action

Antibodies tagged with blue latex

HCG bound to free antibody

The free antibodies are specific for HCG and are colour-labelled. HCG in the urine of a pregnant woman binds to the free antibodies on the surface of the dipstick. The antibodies then travel up the dipstick by capillary action.

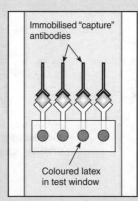

Immobilised "capture" antibodies

Coloured latex in test window

The capture antibodies are specific for the HCG-free antibody complex. The HCG-free antibody complexes travelling up the dipstick are bound by the immobilised **"capture" antibodies**, forming a sandwich. The colour labelled antibodies then create a visible colour change in the test window.

Other Applications of Monoclonal Antibodies

Diagnostic uses

- Detecting the presence of pathogens such as *Chlamydia* and streptococcal bacteria, distinguishing between *Herpesvirus* I and II, and diagnosing AIDS.

- Measuring protein, toxin, or drug levels in serum.

- Blood and tissue typing.

- Detection of antibiotic residues in milk.

Therapeutic uses

- Neutralising endotoxins produced by bacteria in blood infections.

- Used to prevent organ rejection, e.g. in kidney transplants, by interfering with the T cells involved with the rejection of transplanted tissue.

- Used in the treatment of some auto-immune disorders such as rheumatoid arthritis and allergic asthma. The monoclonal antibodies bind to and inactivate factors involved in the cascade leading to the inflammatory response.

- Immunodetection and immunotherapy of cancer. Newer methods specifically target the cell membranes of tumour cells, shrinking solid tumours without harmful side effects.

- Inhibition of platelet clumping, which is used to prevent reclogging of coronary arteries in patients who have undergone angioplasty. The monoclonal antibodies bind to the receptors on the platelet surface that are normally linked by fibrinogen during the clotting process.

4. For each of the following applications, suggest why an antibody-based test or therapy is so valuable:

(a) Detection of toxins or bacteria in perishable foods: _____

_____

_____

(b) Detection of pregnancy without a doctor's prescription: _____

_____

(c) Targeted treatment of tumours in cancer patients: _____

_____

Immunisation

A vaccine is a suspension of microorganisms (or pieces of them) that protects against disease by stimulating the production of antibodies and inducing **immunity**. **Vaccination** (often used synonymously with **immunisation**) is a procedure that provides **artificially acquired active immunity** in the recipient. A concerted vaccination campaign led to the eradication (in 1977) of **smallpox**, the only disease to have been eradicated in this way. Once eradicated, a pathogen is no longer present in the environment and vaccination is no longer necessary. Features of smallpox made it particularly suitable for complete eradication. It was a very recognisable and visible disease, with no long-term, human carriers and no non-human carriers. In addition, people who had not been vaccinated against the disease were identifiable by the absence of a vaccination scar on the upper arm. Disease control (as opposed to eradication) does not necessarily require that everyone be immune. **Herd immunity**, where most of the population is immune, limits outbreaks to sporadic cases because there are too few susceptible individuals to support an epidemic. Vaccination provides effective control over many common bacterial and viral diseases. Viral diseases in particular are best prevented with vaccination, as they cannot be effectively treated once contracted.

Primary and Secondary Responses to Antigens

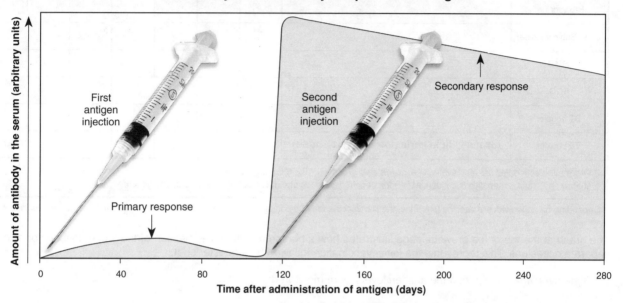

Preventing and Treating Disease

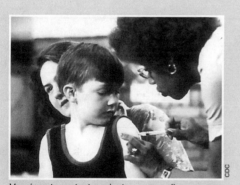

Vaccines to protect against common diseases are administered at various stages during childhood according to an immunisation schedule.

While most vaccinations are given in childhood, adults may be vaccinated against specific diseases (e.g. tuberculosis) if they are in a high risk group or if they are travelling to a region in the world where a disease is prevalent.

Selected Vaccines Used To Prevent Diseases In Humans		
Disease	**Type of vaccine**	**Recommendation**
Diphtheria	Purified diphtheria toxoid	From early childhood and every 10 years for adults
Meningococcal meningitis	Purified polysaccharide of *Neisseria menigitidis*	For people with substantial risk of infection
Whooping cough	Killed cells or fragments of *Bordetella pertussis*	Children prior to school age
Tetanus	Purified tetanus toxoid	14-16 year olds with booster every 10 years
Meningitis caused by *Haemophilus influenzae* b	Polysaccharide from virus conjugated with protein to enhance effectiveness	Early childhood
Influenza	Killed virus (vaccines using genetically engineered antigenic fragments are also being developed)	For chronically ill people, especially with respiratory diseases, or for healthy people over 65 years of age
Measles	Attenuated virus	Early childhood
Mumps	Attenuated virus	Early childhood
Rubella	Attenuated virus	Early childhood; for females of child-bearing age who are not pregnant
Polio	Attenuated or killed virus (enhanced potency type)	Early childhood
Hepatitis B	Antigenic fragments of virus	Early childhood

1. The table below provides a list of the vaccines used in the standard vaccination schedule for children and young adults in the United Kingdom. Additional vaccinations are available for those at high risk of contracting certain diseases.

   (a) List the diseases that each vaccine protects against.

   (b) Determine the ages at which each vaccine should be administered. Place a tick (✔) in each age column as appropriate (the last one has been done for you). You can complete this for your own country if you wish. Schedules are available from www.thebiozone.com/vaccination.html and can be completed and used to replace the one shown.

Vaccination Schedule Available to Children in the United Kingdom

Vaccine	Diseases protected from	Age in months				Age in years		
		2	3	4	12-15	3-5	10-14	13-18
DTP (Triple antigen)								
Hib vaccine*								
OPV (Sabin vaccine)								
MMR								
BCG								
DT booster								
Td booster	Tetanus, diphtheria (low strength dose)							✔

Vaccination schedules are also available **for high risk groups** for the following diseases:
anthrax, hepatitis A, hepatitis B, influenza, pneumococcal disease, typhoid, varicella (chickenpox), and yellow fever.

* Depending on an individual's vaccine tolerance, the Hib vaccine may be conjugated with the DTP vaccine or given as a separate vaccination

2. The graph at the top of the previous page illustrates how a person reacts to the injection of the same antibody on two separate occasions. This represents the initial vaccination followed by a booster shot.

   (a) State over what time period the antigen levels were monitored: _____

   (b) State what happens to the antibody levels after the first injection: _____

   _____

   (c) State what happens to the antibody levels after the booster shot: _____

   _____

   (d) Explain why the second injection has a markedly different effect: _____

   _____

3. The whole question of whether young children should be immunised has been a point of hot debate with some parents. The parents that do not want their children immunised have strongly held reasons for doing so. In a balanced way, explore the arguments for and against childhood immunisation:

   (a) State clearly the benefits from childhood immunisation: _____

   _____

   _____

   (b) Explain why some parents are concerned about immunising their children: _____

   _____

   _____

4. Consult your family doctor or medical centre and list three vaccinations that are recommended for travellers to overseas destinations with high risk of infectious disease:

   (a) Country/region: _____ Vaccine required: _____

   (b) Country/region: _____ Vaccine required: _____

   (c) Country/region: _____ Vaccine required: _____

Types of Vaccine

There are two basic types of vaccine: subunit vaccines and whole-agent vaccines. **Whole-agent vaccines** contain complete nonvirulent microbes, either **inactivated** (killed), or alive but **attenuated** (weakened). Attenuated viruses make very effective vaccines and often provide life-long immunity without the need for booster immunisations. Killed viruses are less effective, and many vaccines of this sort have now been replaced by newer subunit vaccines. **Subunit vaccines** contain only the parts of the pathogen that induce the immune response. They are safer than attenuated vaccines because they cannot reproduce in the recipient, and they produce fewer adverse effects because they contain little or no extra material. Subunit vaccines can be made using a variety of methods, including cell fragmentation (*acellular vaccines*), inactivation of toxins (*toxoids*), genetic engineering (*recombinant vaccines*), and combination with antigenic proteins (*conjugated vaccines*). In all cases, the subunit vaccine loses its ability to cause disease but retains its antigenic properties so that it is still effective in inducing an immune response. Some of the most promising types of vaccine under development are the **DNA vaccines**, consisting of naked DNA (encoding the antigen) which is injected into the body and produces an antigenic protein. So far, no experimental trials have provoked an immunological response strong enough to protect against disease, and their usefulness remains unproven.

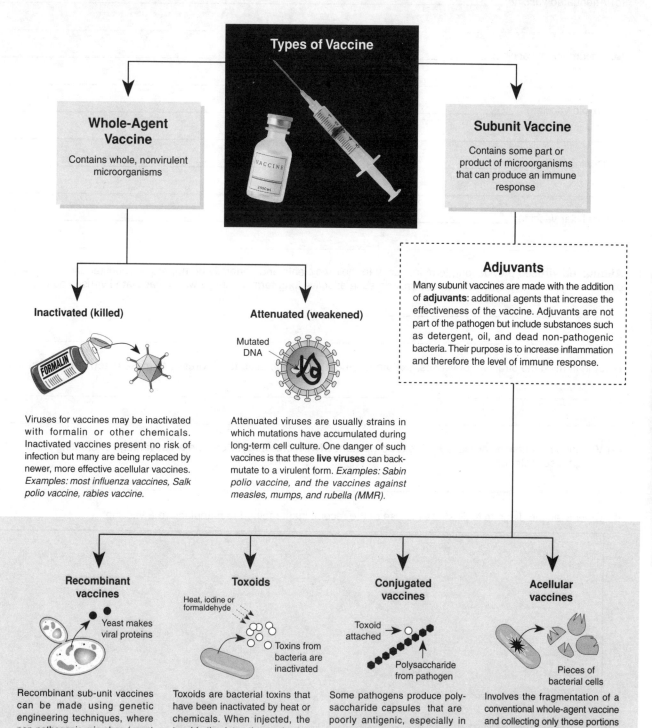

Types of Vaccine

Whole-Agent Vaccine

Contains whole, nonvirulent microorganisms

Subunit Vaccine

Contains some part or product of microorganisms that can produce an immune response

Adjuvants

Many subunit vaccines are made with the addition of **adjuvants**: additional agents that increase the effectiveness of the vaccine. Adjuvants are not part of the pathogen but include substances such as detergent, oil, and dead non-pathogenic bacteria. Their purpose is to increase inflammation and therefore the level of immune response.

Inactivated (killed)

Viruses for vaccines may be inactivated with formalin or other chemicals. Inactivated vaccines present no risk of infection but many are being replaced by newer, more effective acellular vaccines. *Examples: most influenza vaccines, Salk polio vaccine, rabies vaccine.*

Attenuated (weakened)

Mutated DNA

Attenuated viruses are usually strains in which mutations have accumulated during long-term cell culture. One danger of such vaccines is that these **live viruses** can back-mutate to a virulent form. *Examples: Sabin polio vaccine, and the vaccines against measles, mumps, and rubella (MMR).*

Recombinant vaccines

Yeast makes viral proteins

Recombinant sub-unit vaccines can be made using genetic engineering techniques, where non-pathogenic microbes (yeast and bacteria) are programmed to make a desired antigenic fraction. *Example: hepatitis B vaccine.*

Toxoids

Heat, iodine or formaldehyde

Toxins from bacteria are inactivated

Toxoids are bacterial toxins that have been inactivated by heat or chemicals. When injected, the toxoid stimulates the production of antitoxins (antibodies) that neutralise any circulating toxin. *Examples: diphtheria vaccine, tetanus vaccine.*

Conjugated vaccines

Toxoid attached

Polysaccharide from pathogen

Some pathogens produce poly-saccharide capsules that are poorly antigenic, especially in young children. To enhance their effectiveness, they are combined with proteins such as toxoids from other pathogens. *Example: vaccine against Haemophilus influenzae b.*

Acellular vaccines

Pieces of bacterial cells

Involves the fragmentation of a conventional whole-agent vaccine and collecting only those portions that contain the desired antigens. Because the complete cells are not used, infection is not possible. *Examples: newer whooping cough and typhoid vaccines.*

Preventing and Treating Disease

Code: RA 3

1. Describe briefly **how** each of the following types of vaccine are made and name an **example** of each:

   (a) Whole-agent vaccine: _____

   (b) Subunit vaccine: _____

   (c) Inactivated vaccine: _____

   (d) Attenuated vaccine: _____

   (e) Recombinant vaccine: _____

   (f) Toxoid vaccine: _____

   (g) Conjugated vaccine: _____

   (h) Acellular vaccine: _____

2. **Attenuated viruses** provide long term immunity to their recipients and generally do not require booster shots. Suggest a possible reason why attenuated viruses provide such effective long-term immunity when inactivated viruses do not:

3. Bearing in mind the structure of viruses, explain why **heat** cannot be used to kill viruses to make **inactivated vaccines**:

4. (a) Vaccines may now be produced using **recombinant DNA technology**. Describe an advantage of creating vaccines using these methods:

   (b) Draw a simple diagram to illustrate the use of the recombinant method to manufacture a vaccine:

Edible Vaccines

Although still a few years away, the development of edible vaccines produced by transgenic plants will overcome many of the problems faced when using traditional, injectable vaccines. Plants engineered to contain the vaccine can be grown locally, in the area where vaccination is required, overcoming the logistic and economic problems of transporting prepared vaccines over long distances. Most importantly, edible vaccines do not require syringes, saving money and eliminating the risk of infection from contaminated needles. One method used to generate edible vaccines relies on the bacterium *Agrobacterium tumefaciens* to deliver the genes for viral or bacterial antigens into plant cells. The diagram below illustrates this process using potatoes.

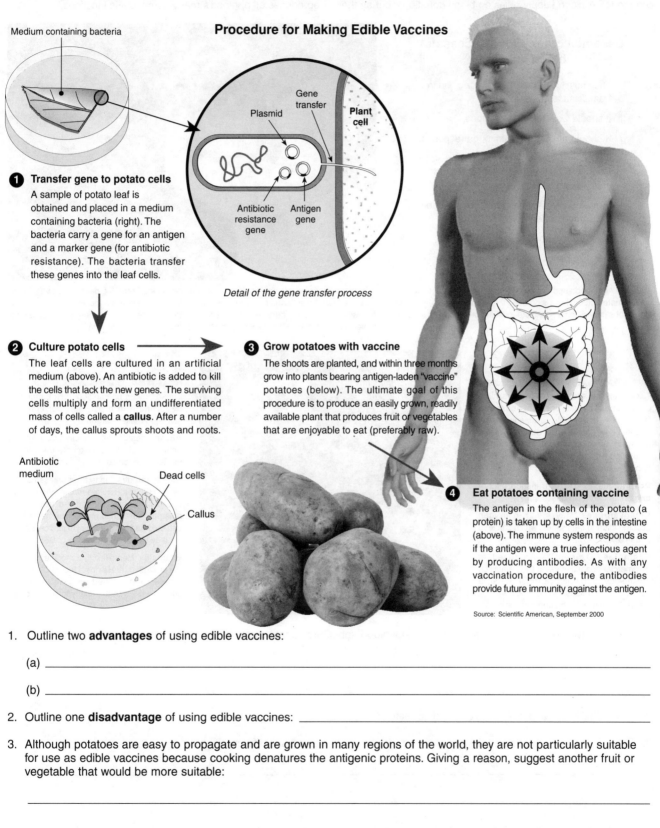

Procedure for Making Edible Vaccines

Medium containing bacteria

Detail of the gene transfer process

Plasmid

Gene transfer

Plant cell

Antibiotic resistance gene

Antigen gene

1 **Transfer gene to potato cells**

A sample of potato leaf is obtained and placed in a medium containing bacteria (right). The bacteria carry a gene for an antigen and a marker gene (for antibiotic resistance). The bacteria transfer these genes into the leaf cells.

2 **Culture potato cells**

The leaf cells are cultured in an artificial medium (above). An antibiotic is added to kill the cells that lack the new genes. The surviving cells multiply and form an undifferentiated mass of cells called a **callus**. After a number of days, the callus sprouts shoots and roots.

3 **Grow potatoes with vaccine**

The shoots are planted, and within three months grow into plants bearing antigen-laden "vaccine" potatoes (below). The ultimate goal of this procedure is to produce an easily grown, readily available plant that produces fruit or vegetables that are enjoyable to eat (preferably raw).

Antibiotic medium

Dead cells

Callus

4 **Eat potatoes containing vaccine**

The antigen in the flesh of the potato (a protein) is taken up by cells in the intestine (above). The immune system responds as if the antigen were a true infectious agent by producing antibodies. As with any vaccination procedure, the antibodies provide future immunity against the antigen.

Source: Scientific American, September 2000

Preventing and Treating Disease

1. Outline two **advantages** of using edible vaccines:

   (a) _____

   (b) _____

2. Outline one **disadvantage** of using edible vaccines: _____

3. Although potatoes are easy to propagate and are grown in many regions of the world, they are not particularly suitable for use as edible vaccines because cooking denatures the antigenic proteins. Giving a reason, suggest another fruit or vegetable that would be more suitable:

   _____

   _____

4. Explain why a gene for antibiotic resistance is added to the bacterium: _____

   _____

The Search for Blood Substitutes

Blood's essential homeostatic role is evident when considering the problems encountered when large volumes of blood are lost. Transfusion of whole blood (see photograph below) or plasma is an essential part of many medical procedures, e.g. after trauma or surgery, or as a regular part of the treatment for some disorders (e.g. thalassaemia). This makes blood a valuable commodity. A blood supply relies on blood donations, but as the demand for blood increases, the availability of donors continues to decline. This decline is partly due to more stringent screening of donors for diseases such as HIV/AIDS, hepatitis, and variant CJD. The inadequacy of blood supplies has made the search for a safe, effective blood substitute the focus of much research. Despite some possibilities, no currently available substitute reproduces all of blood's many homeostatic functions.

Essential criteria for a successful blood substitute

☐ The substitute should be non-toxic and free from diseases.

☐ It should work for all blood types.

☐ It should not cause an immune response.

☐ It should remain in circulation until the blood volume is restored and then it should be safely excreted.

☐ It must be easily transported and suitable for storage under normal refrigeration.

☐ It should have a long shelf life.

☐ It should perform some or all of blood tasks.

Photo Hemosol Inc. Information courtesy of DRDC Toronto

A shortfall in blood supplies, greater demand, and public fear of contaminated blood, have increased the need for a safe, effective blood substitute. Such a substitute must fulfil strict criteria (above).

A researcher displays a haemoglobin based artificial blood product, developed by Defence R&D Canada, Toronto and now produced under license by Hemosol Inc. Human testing and marketing has now progressed successfully into advanced trials. A human haemoglobin molecule is pictured in the background. Photo with permission from Hemosol inc.

Chemical based

These rely on synthetic oxygen-carrying compounds called **perfluorocarbons** (PFCs). PFCs are able to dissolve large quantities of gases. They do not dissolve freely in the plasma, so they must be emulsified with an agent that enables them to be dispersed in the blood.

Advantages: PFCs can transport a lot of oxygen, and transfer gases quickly.

Disadvantages: May result in oxygen accumulation in the tissues, which can lead to damage.

Examples: Oxygent™: Produced in commercial quantities using PFC emulsion technology; Perflubon (a PFC), water, a surfactant, and salts, homogenized into a stable, biologically compatible emulsion.

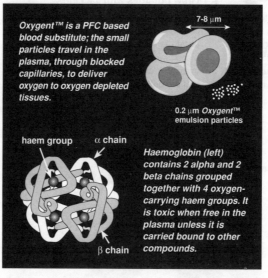

Oxygent™ is a PFC based blood substitute; the small particles travel in the plasma, through blocked capillaries, to deliver oxygen to oxygen depleted tissues.

7-8 µm

0.2 µm *Oxygent™* emulsion particles

haem group   α chain

Haemoglobin (left) contains 2 alpha and 2 beta chains grouped together with 4 oxygen-carrying haem groups. It is toxic when free in the plasma unless it is carried bound to other compounds.

β chain

Haemoglobin based

These rely on haemoglobin (Hb), modified by joining it to a polymer (polyethylene glycol) to make it larger.

Advantages: Modified haemoglobin should better be able to approximate the various properties of blood.

Disadvantages: Hb is toxic unless carried within RBCs; it requires modification before it can be safely transported free in the plasma. Substitutes made from human Hb use outdated blood as the Hb source. Bovine Hb may transmit diseases (e.g. BSE).

Examples: Hemolink™, a modified human Hb produced by Hemosol Inc. in California. Research is focused on developing cell culture lines with the ability to produce Hb.

1. Describe two essential features of a successful blood substitute, identifying briefly why the feature is important:

   (a) _____

   (b) _____

2. Name the two classes of artificial blood substitutes: _____

3. Discuss the advantages and risks associated with the use of blood substitutes: _____

   _____

   _____

   _____

   _____

   _____

The Human Genome Project

The **Human Genome Project** (HGP) is a publicly funded venture involving many different organisations throughout the world. In 1998, Celera Genomics in the USA began a competing project, as a commercial venture, in a race to be the first to determine the human genome sequence. In 2000, both organisations reached the first draft stage, and the entire genome is now available as a high quality (golden standard) sequence. In addition to determining the order of bases in the human genome, genes are being identified, sequenced, and mapped (their specific chromosomal location identified). The next challenge is to assign functions to the identified genes. By identifying and studying the protein products of genes (a field known as **proteomics**),

scientists can develop a better understanding of genetic disorders. Long term benefits of the HGP are both medical and non-medical (overleaf). Many biotechnology companies have taken out patents on gene sequences. This practice is controversial because it restricts the use of the sequence information to the patent holders. Other genome sequencing projects have arisen as a result of the initiative to sequence the human one. A controversial project to map the differences between racial and ethnic groups is the **Human Genome Diversity Project** (HGDP). It aims to understand the degree of diversity amongst individuals in the human species. It is still in its planning stages, seeking the best way to achieve its goals.

Gene Mapping

This process involves determining the precise position of a gene on a chromosome. Once the position is known, it can be shown on a diagram.

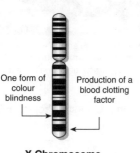

One form of colour blindness · Production of a blood clotting factor

X Chromosome

Equipment used for DNA Sequencing

Banks of PCR machines prepare DNA for the sequencing gel stage. The DNA is amplified and chemically tagged (to make the DNA fluoresce and enable visualisation on a gel).

Banks of DNA sequencing gels and powerful computers are used to determine the base order in DNA.

Count of Mapped Genes

The length and number of mapped genes to date for each chromosome are tabulated below. The entire human genome contains approximately 20 000-25 000 genes.

Chromosome	Length (Mb)	No. of Mapped Genes
1	263	1871
2	255	1113
3	214	964
4	203	613
5	194	782
6	183	1216
7	171	995
8	155	589
9	145	802
10	144	872
11	144	1162
12	143	892
13	114	290
14	109	1013
15	106	509
16	98	656
17	92	1034
18	85	302
19	67	1128
20	72	599
21	50	386
22	56	501
X	164	1020
Y	59	122
Total:		**19 431**

As at: 19 March 2006 For an update see:
http://gdbwww.gdb.org/gdbreports/ CountGeneByChromosome.html

Examples of Mapped Genes

The positions of an increasing number of genes have been mapped onto human chromosomes (see below). Sequence variations can cause or contribute to identifiable disorders. Note that chromosome 21 (the smallest human chromosome) has a relatively low gene density, while others are gene rich. This is possibly why trisomy 21 (Down syndrome) is one of the few viable human autosomal trisomies.

Key

☐ Variable regions (heterochromatin)

■ Regions reflecting the unique patterns of light and dark bands seen on stained chromosomes

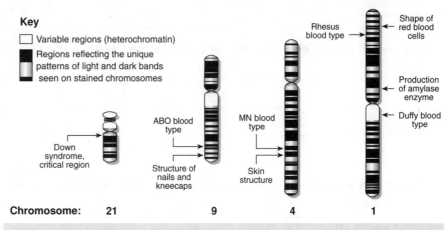

Down syndrome, critical region — ABO blood type — Structure of nails and kneecaps — MN blood type — Skin structure — Rhesus blood type — Shape of red blood cells — Production of amylase enzyme — Duffy blood type

Chromosome: 21 · 9 · 4 · 1

The aim of the HGP was to produce a continuous block of sequence information for each chromosome. Initially the sequence information was obtained to draft quality, with an error rate of 1 in 1000 bases. The **Gold Standard sequence**, with an error rate of <1 per 100 000 bases, was completed in October 2004. Key results of the research are:

- The analysis suggests that there are perhaps only 20 000-25 000 protein-coding genes in our human genome.
- The number of gaps has been reduced 400-fold to only 341
- It covers 99% of the gene containing parts of the genome and is 99.999% accurate.
- The new sequence correctly identifies almost all known genes (99.74%).
- Its accuracy and completeness allows systematic searches for causes of disease.

Preventing and Treating Disease

Code: RA 2

Benefits and ethical issues arising from the Human Genome Project

Medical benefits

- Improved **diagnosis** of disease and predisposition to disease by genetic testing.
- Better identification of disease carriers, through genetic testing.
- Better **drugs** can be designed using knowledge of protein structure (from gene sequence information) rather than by trial and error.
- Greater possibility of successfully using **gene therapy** to correct genetic disorders.

Non-medical benefits

- Greater knowledge of **family relationships** through genetic testing, e.g. paternity testing in family courts.
- Advances **forensic science** through analysis of DNA at crime scenes.
- Improved knowledge of the evolutionary relationships between humans and other organisms, which will help to develop better, more accurate classification systems.

Possible ethical issues

- It is unclear whether third parties, e.g. health insurers, have rights to genetic test results.
- If treatment is unavailable for a disease, genetic knowledge about it may have no use.
- Genetic tests are costly, and there is no easy answer as to who should pay for them.
- Genetic information is hereditary so knowledge of an individual's own genome has implications for members of their family.

Couples can already have a limited range of genetic tests to determine the risk of having offspring with some disease-causing mutations.

When DNA sequences are available for humans and their ancestors, comparative analysis may provide clues about human evolution.

Legislation is needed to ensure that there is no discrimination on the basis of genetic information, e.g. at work or for health insurance.

1. Briefly describe the objectives of the Human Genome Project (HGP) and the Human Genome Diversity Project (HGDP):

   HGP: _____

   _____

   HGDP: _____

2. Suggest a reason why indigenous peoples around the world are reluctant to provide DNA samples for the HGDP:

   _____

   _____

3. Describe two possible **benefits** of Human Genome Project (HGP):

   (a) Medical: _____

   _____

   (b) Non-medical: _____

   _____

4. Explain what is meant by **proteomics** and explain its significance to the HGP and the ongoing benefits arising from it:

   _____

   _____

   _____

   _____

5. Suggest two possible points of view for one of the **ethical issues** described in the list above:

   (a) _____

   _____

   (b) _____

   _____

Gene Therapy

Gene therapy refers to the application of gene technology to correct or replace defective genes. It was first envisioned as a treatment, or even a cure, for genetic disorders, but it could also be used to treat a wide range of diseases, including those that resist conventional treatments. Gene therapy may operate by providing a correctly working version of a faulty gene or by adding a **novel gene** to perform a corrective role. In other cases, gene expression may be blocked in order to control cellular (or viral) activity. About two thirds of currently approved gene therapy procedures are targeting cancer, about one quarter aim to treat genetic disorders, such as cystic fibrosis, and the remainder are attempting to provide relief for infectious diseases. Gene therapy requires a **gene delivery system**; a way to transfer the gene to the patient's cells. This may be achieved using a infectious agent such as a virus; a technique called **transfection**. A promising development has been the recent approval for gene therapy to be used in treating tumours in cancer patients. Severe combined immune deficiency syndrome (SCIDS) has also shown improvement after gene therapy. Infants treated for this inherited, normally lethal condition have become healthy young adults (see below). Gene therapy involving **somatic cells** may be therapeutic, but the genetic changes are not inherited. The transfection of **stem cells**, rather than mature somatic cells, achieves a longer persistence of therapy in patients. In the future, the introduction of corrective genes into **germline cells** will enable genetic corrections to be inherited.

Gene Delivery Using Extracted Cells

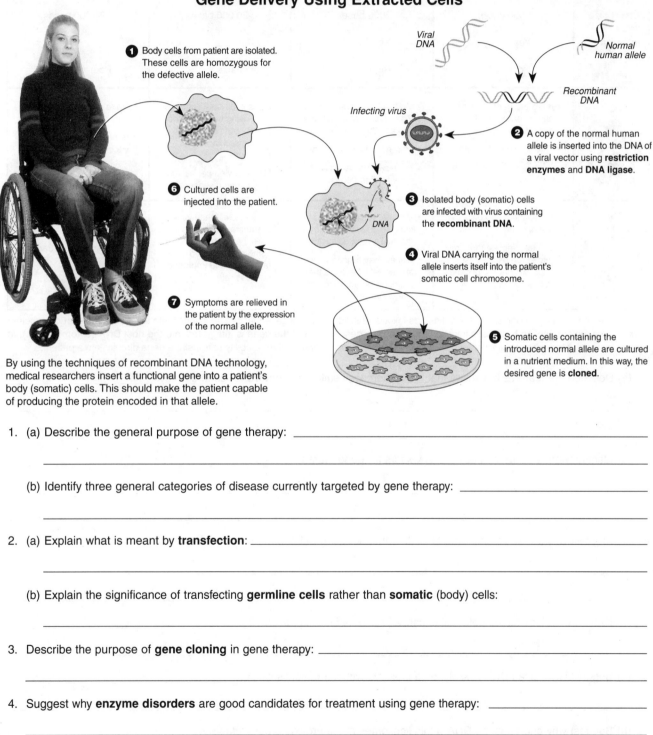

1 Body cells from patient are isolated. These cells are homozygous for the defective allele.

Viral DNA

Normal human allele

Recombinant DNA

Infecting virus

2 A copy of the normal human allele is inserted into the DNA of a viral vector using **restriction enzymes** and **DNA ligase**.

6 Cultured cells are injected into the patient.

DNA

3 Isolated body (somatic) cells are infected with virus containing the **recombinant DNA**.

4 Viral DNA carrying the normal allele inserts itself into the patient's somatic cell chromosome.

7 Symptoms are relieved in the patient by the expression of the normal allele.

5 Somatic cells containing the introduced normal allele are cultured in a nutrient medium. In this way, the desired gene is **cloned**.

By using the techniques of recombinant DNA technology, medical researchers insert a functional gene into a patient's body (somatic) cells. This should make the patient capable of producing the protein encoded in that allele.

1. (a) Describe the general purpose of gene therapy: _____

   _____

   (b) Identify three general categories of disease currently targeted by gene therapy: _____

   _____

2. (a) Explain what is meant by **transfection**: _____

   _____

   (b) Explain the significance of transfecting **germline cells** rather than **somatic** (body) cells:

   _____

3. Describe the purpose of **gene cloning** in gene therapy: _____

   _____

4. Suggest why **enzyme disorders** are good candidates for treatment using gene therapy: _____

   _____

   _____

Vectors for Gene Therapy

Gene therapy usually requires a **vector** (carrier) to introduce the DNA. The majority of approved clinical gene therapy protocols (63%) employ **retroviral vectors** to deliver the selected gene to the target cells, although there is considerable risk in using these vectors (below). Other widely used vectors include adenoviral vectors (16%), and liposomes (13%). The remaining 8% employ a variety of vector systems, the majority of which include injection of naked plasmid DNA.

Vectors That Can Be Used For Gene Therapy			
 **Retrovirus**	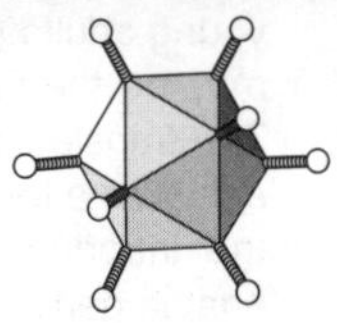 **Adenovirus**	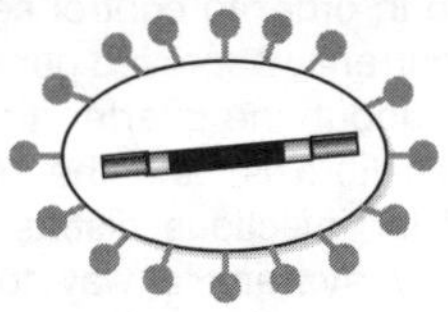 **Liposome**	 **Naked DNA**
Insert size: 8000 bases	8000 bases	>20 000 bases	>20 000 bases
Integration: Yes	No	No	No
In vivo delivery: Poor	High	Variable	Poor
Advantages • Integrate genes into the chromosomes of the human host cell. • Offers chance for long-term stability.	• Modified for gene therapy, they infect human cells and express the normal gene. • Most do not cause disease. • Have a large capacity to carry foreign genes.	• Liposomes seek out target cells using sugars in their membranes that are recognised by cell receptors. • Have no viral genes that may cause disease.	• Have no viral genes that may cause disease. • Expected to be useful for vaccination.
Disadvantages • Many infect only cells that are dividing. • Genes integrate randomly into chromosomes, so might disrupt useful genes in the host cell.	• Viruses may have poor survival due to attack by the host's immune system. • Genes may function only sporadically because they are not integrated into host cell's chromosome.	• Less efficient than viruses at transferring genes into cells, but recent work on using sugars to aid targeting have improved success rate.	• Unstable in most tissues of the body. • Inefficient at gene transfer.

In the table above, the following terms are defined as follows: **Naked DNA**: the genes are applied by ballistic injection (firing using a gene gun) or by regular hypodermic injection of plasmid DNA. **Insert size**: size of gene that can be inserted into the vector. **Integration**: whether or not the gene is integrated into the host DNA (chromosomes). **In vivo delivery**: ability to transfer a gene directly into a patient.

1. (a) Describe the features of viruses that make them well suited as **vectors** for gene therapy: _____

_____

_____

(b) Identify two problems with using viral vectors for gene therapy: _____

_____

_____

2. (a) Suggest why it may be beneficial for a (therapeutic) gene to integrate into the patient's chromosome: _____

_____

_____

(b) Explain why this has the potential to cause problems for the patient: _____

_____

3. (a) Suggest why naked DNA is likely to be unstable within a patient's tissues: _____

_____

(b) Suggest why enclosing the DNA within liposomes might provide greater stability: _____

_____

Gene Delivery Systems

The mapping of the human genome has improved the feasibility of gene therapy as a option for treating an increasingly wide range of diseases, but it remains technically difficult to deliver genes successfully to a patient. Even after a gene has been identified, cloned, and transferred to a patient, it must be expressed normally. To date, the success of gene therapy has been generally poor, and improvements have been short-lived or counteracted by adverse side effects. Inserted genes may reach only about 1% of target cells and those that reach their destination may work inefficiently and produce too little protein, too slowly to be of benefit. In addition, many patients react immunologically to the vectors used in gene transfer. Much of the current research is focussed on improving the efficiency of gene transfer and expression. One of the first gene therapy trials was for **cystic fibrosis** (CF). CF was an obvious candidate for gene therapy because, in most cases, the disease is caused by a single, known gene mutation. However, despite its early promise, gene therapy for this disease has been disappointing (below).

Gene Therapy as a Potential Treatment for Cystic Fibrosis (CF)

In cystic fibrosis, a gene mutation causes the body to produce an abnormally thick, sticky mucus that accumulates in the lungs and intestines. The identification and isolation of the CF gene in 1989 meant that scientists could look for ways in which to correct the genetic defect rather than just treating the symptoms using traditional therapies.

In trials, normal genes were isolated and inserted into patients using vectors such as **adenoviruses** and **liposomes**.

In order to prevent the progressive and ultimately lethal lung damage, the main target of CF gene therapy is the lung. The viral vector was piped directly into the lung, whereas the liposomes were inhaled in a spray formulation. The results of these trials were disappointing; on average, there was only a 25% correction, the effects were short lived, and the benefits were quickly reversed. Alarmingly, the adenovirus used in one of the trials led to the death of one patient.

Source: Cystic Fibrosis Trust, UK.

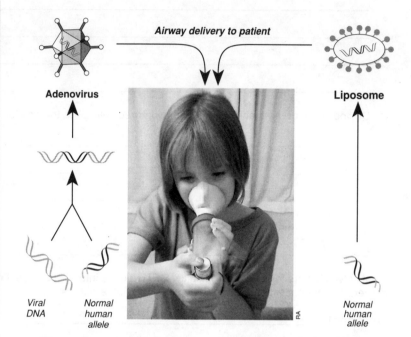

Airway delivery to patient

Adenovirus

Liposome

Viral DNA · Normal human allele

Normal human allele

An **adenovirus** that normally causes colds is genetically modified to make it safe and to carry the normal (unmutated) CFTR ('cystic fibrosis') gene.

Liposomes are tiny fat globules. Normal CF genes are enclosed in liposomes, which fuse with plasma membranes and deliver the genes into the cells.

Gene Delivery Systems Used In Human Patients

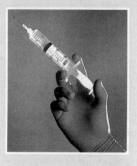

Hypodermic needle injection

- Injection of the vectors directly into the bloodstream or other organs of the patient. Vectors injected into the blood travel throughout the body and may be taken up by the target cells.
- Injections of plasmid DNA into thymus, skin, cardiac muscle and skeletal muscle have already proved successful in non-human trials (mice and primates).

Aerosol

- Aerosols and nebulisers offer an effective spread and efficient delivery of the vector to the site of certain target cells (especially in the respiratory tract).
- Used in trials of gene therapy for cystic fibrosis, but effective only on epithelial cells that can be reached by the aerosol.

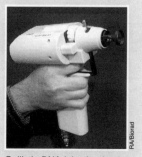

Ballistic DNA injection is also called microprojectile gene transfer, the gene-gun, or particle bombardment method.

Ballistic DNA injection

- Plasmid DNA encoding the gene of interest is coated onto microbeads, and these are 'fired' at the target cells using gas pressure or a high voltage discharge.
- Used to transfer genes to a wide variety of cell lines (*ex vivo*) or directly into surgically exposed tissue (*in vivo*).
- May be used in DNA-based vaccines to prevent infectious diseases or cancer.
- Allows delivery of precise DNA dosages. However, genes delivered by this method are expressed transiently and there is considerable cell damage at the centre of the discharge site.

An incubator for culturing cell lines (ex vivo).

©1999 University of Kansas Office of University Relations

Gene delivery to extracted cells and cell culture

- Target cells are isolated from tissue. Non-specific gene delivery is applied to the total cell population or as a microinjection of DNA into the nucleus of a single cell.
- Cells that have taken up the normal allele are cultured outside the body (*ex vivo*) and re-injected into the patient.
- The expression of the normal allele relieves symptoms of the disease.

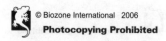

1. A great deal of current research is being devoted to discovering a gene therapy solution to treat **cystic fibrosis** (CF):

    (a) Describe the symptoms of CF: _____

    _____

    _____

    (b) Explain why this genetic disease has been so eagerly targeted by gene therapy researchers: _____

    _____

    _____

    _____

    _____

    (c) Outline some of the problems so far encountered with gene therapy for CF: _____

    _____

    _____

    _____

    _____

    _____

2. Identify two vectors for introducing healthy CFTR genes into CF patients. For each vector, outline how it might be delivered to the patient and describe potential problems with its use:

    (a) Vector 1: _____

    Delivery: _____

    Problems: _____

    _____

    _____

    (b) Vector 2: _____

    Delivery: _____

    Problems: _____

    _____

    _____

3. Changes made to chromosomes as a result of gene therapy involving somatic cells are not inherited. Germ-line gene therapy has the potential to cure disease, but the risks and benefits are still not clear. For each of the points outlined below, evaluate the risk of germ-line gene therapy relative to somatic cell gene therapy and explain your answer:

    (a) Chance of interfering with an essential gene function: _____

    _____

    _____

    _____

    (b) Misuse of the therapy to selectively alter phenotype: _____

    _____

    _____

    _____

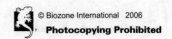

Correcting Heart Problems

Over the last decade the death rates from CVD have slowly declined, despite an increase in its prevalence. This reduction in mortality has been achieved partly through better management and treatment of the disease. Medical technology now provides the means to correct many heart problems, even if only temporarily. Some symptoms of CVD, arising as a result of blockages to the coronary arteries, are now commonly treated using techniques such as coronary bypass surgery and angioplasty. Other cardiac disorders, such as disorders of heartbeat, are frequently treated using cardiac pacemakers. Valve defects, which are often congenital, can be successfully corrected with surgical valve replacement. The latest technology, still in its trial phase, involves non-surgical replacement of aortic valves. The procedure, known as percutaneous (through the skin) heart valve replacement, will greatly reduce the trauma associated with correcting these particular heart disorders.

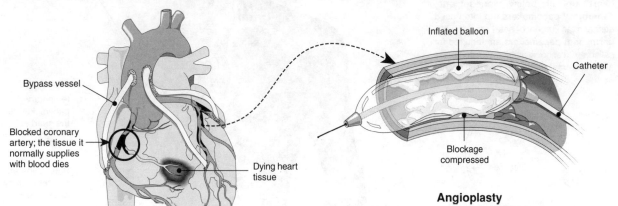

Coronary Bypass Surgery

Commonly used surgery to bypass blocked coronary arteries with blood vessels from elsewhere in the body (e.g. leg vein or mammary artery). Sometimes, double or triple bypasses are performed.

Angioplasty

Angioplasty is an alternative procedure used for some patients with coronary artery disease. A balloon tipped catheter is placed via the aorta into the coronary artery. The balloon is inflated to reduce the blockage of the artery and later removed. Heparin (an anticlotting agent) is given to prevent the formation of blood clots. The death rate from complications is about 1%.

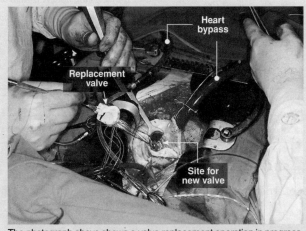

The photograph above shows a valve replacement operation in progress. The valve can be seen threaded up and ready for placement. Two large tubes bypass the heart so that circulation to the lungs and rest of the body is maintained during the operation.

Replacement Heart Valves

Tissue valve   Ball valve   Disc valve

Artificial valves can be of two types: **biological (tissue) valves** and **synthetic valves**. Tissue valves are usually made of animal tissue such as pig tissue. They do not last long (7-10 years) but there are fewer problems with blood clotting and tissue rejection. For these reasons, they are often used in older patients who would not need another replacement in their lifetime. Synthetic ball or disc valves are constructed from non-biological materials. Such valves last a long time but tend to create blood clots (raising the risk of stroke). Used on younger patients, they must take long-term anti-clotting drugs.

1. Explain why patients who have undergone coronary bypass surgery or angioplasty require careful supervision of their diet and lifestyle following the operation, even though their problem has been alleviated:

_____

_____

2. (a) State the type of valve that would be used for an elderly patient needing a valve replacement: _____

   (b) Explain the reasons for your answer: _____

   _____

3. Explain the problems associated with the use of each type of replacement valve:

   (a) Tissue valves: _____

   (b) Synthetic valves: _____

Cardiac Pacemakers

A cardiac pacemaker is sometimes required to maintain an effective heart rate in cases where the heart beats irregularly or too slowly (as in the case of heart block, see the lower trace, right). Pacemakers provide regular electrical stimulation of the heart muscle so that it contracts and relaxes with a normal rhythm. They stand by until the heart rate falls below a pre-set rate. **Temporary pacemakers** are often used after cardiac surgery or heart attacks, while **permanent pacemakers** are required for patients with ongoing problems. Pacemakers allow a normal (even strenuous) lifestyle.

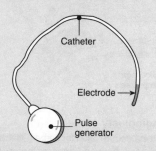

Catheter

Electrode →

Pulse generator

Both permanent and temporary pacemakers consist of a **pulse generator** and a catheter (flexible wire) with electrodes that deliver the stimulus to the heart muscle. The pulse generator contains a small battery and an electronic system to monitor heart activity.

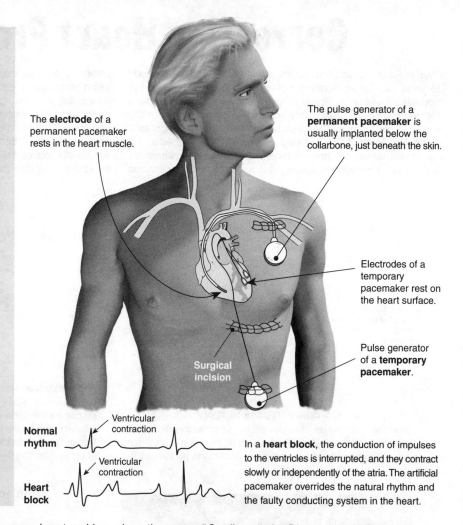

The **electrode** of a permanent pacemaker rests in the heart muscle.

The pulse generator of a **permanent pacemaker** is usually implanted below the collarbone, just beneath the skin.

Electrodes of a temporary pacemaker rest on the heart surface.

Pulse generator of a **temporary pacemaker**.

Surgical incision

Normal rhythm

Ventricular contraction

Heart block

Ventricular contraction

In a **heart block**, the conduction of impulses to the ventricles is interrupted, and they contract slowly or independently of the atria. The artificial pacemaker overrides the natural rhythm and the faulty conducting system in the heart.

4. Describe two techniques used to diagnose heart problems (see the pages "*Cardiovascular Disease*" and "*Diagnosing Medical Problems*" for help if necessary):

   (a) _____

   _____

   (b) _____

   _____

5. Describe two modern techniques for treatment of the effects of atherosclerosis in the coronary arteries:

   (a) _____

   _____

   _____

   (b) _____

   _____

   _____

6. Explain why it is necessary for the heart to receive regular electrical stimulation: _____

   _____

   _____

7. (a) Describe the purpose of a cardiac pacemaker, explaining how it achieves its effect: _____

   _____

   (b) Explain why a temporary pacemaker is often useful for a short time after cardiac surgery: _____

   _____

Organ Transplants

Transplant surgery involves the replacement of a diseased tissue or organ with a healthy, living substitute. The tissue or organ is usually taken from a person who has just died, although some (e.g. blood, kidneys, bone marrow) can be taken from living donors. Around the world, more than 100 000 major organs have been transplanted, mostly in the past few decades. About 80% of patients are alive and well one year after the transplantation, and most survive at least 5 years. There is always a great shortage of donors for organ transplants. Recently, there has been much concern over an emerging black market in body organs and tissue. Attempts to carry out transplants of organs from other species into humans (**xenotransplantation**) have not

been very successful due to rejection, although there are hopes that **genetically modified** pigs may be used to produce organs especially altered to overcome immune rejection in human recipients. The success of organ transplants today has been the result of more effective **immunosuppressant drugs**, improved **tissue-typing**, and better techniques for organ preservation and transport. With the advent of **tissue engineering** and stem cell technology, researchers are rapidly moving towards creating semisynthetic, living organs that may be used as human replacement parts. Artificial skin has already been successfully developed, and more complex organs, such as the liver, may be possible using the same technology within 20 years.

Organ Transplants

Currently, there are five organs that are routinely transplanted. In addition to organs, whole hand transplants and, recently, **face transplants** are now possible. These transplants require careful connection of blood vessels, skin, muscles, and bone, tendons, and other connective tissues. Performing face transplants, for example on burn victims, also involves addressing a number of ethical concerns.

Heart (H): Replacement after heart failure due to heart attack, viral infections of the heart, or congenital. irreparable defects.

Lungs (Ls): Replace organs damaged by cystic fibrosis or emphysema. Typically, lungs are transplanted together, but single lung transplants and heart-lung transplants are also possible.

Liver (Li): Substitute for a liver destroyed by cirrhosis, congenital defects, or hepatitis.

Pancreas (P): Restores insulin production in Type I diabetics (caused by autoimmune destruction of the insulin producing cells of the pancreas).

Kidneys: Eliminates need for dialysis in patients suffering from renal failure, diabetes, high blood pressure, inherited illnesses, and infection.

Hands: On the 24th January 1999, Matthew Scott was America's first hand transplant patient. A year and a half after the operation, he could sense temperature, pressure and pain, and could write, turn the pages of a newspaper, tie shoelaces and throw a baseball.

Tissue Transplants

A large number of tissues are currently used in transplant procedures. An estimated 200 patients can potentially benefit from the organs and tissues donated from a single body.

Cornea: Transplants can restore impaired vision.

Dental powder: This tissue is prepared to help rebuild defects in the mandible (which supports the teeth).

Jaw: The mandible is used in facial reconstruction.

Ear bones: The three bones of the inner ear can be transplanted to improve some forms of deafness.

Pericardium: The pericardium surrounding the heart is made of tough tissue that can be used to cover the brain after surgery. Transplants of the brain coverings themselves are no longer performed because of the risk of transmitting prion infections.

Blood and blood vessels: Blood transfusions are transplants of blood tissue. Blood vessels, mostly veins, can be transplanted to reroute blood around blockages in the body.

Bone marrow: Marrow is extracted from living donors and used to help people with a wide variety of illnesses, such as leukaemia.

Bones: Long bones of the arms and legs can be used in limb reconstruction; ribs can be used for spinal fusions and facial repair.

Cartilage and ligaments: Orthopaedic surgeons use these materials to rebuild ankle, knee, hip, elbow and shoulder joints.

Hip joints: Joints can be reconstructed by transplanting the head of the femur.

Skin: Skin can be used as a temporary covering for burn injuries until the patient's own skin grows back.

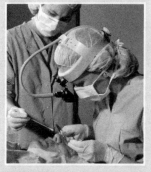

Corneal transplants can be used to restore sight in patients with damaged vision. The cornea naturally has a poor blood supply so rejection is less of a problem than with some other tissues

For many amputees, being fitted with an artificial limb is the first step towards mobility. In the future, such prostheses may be replaced with limb transplants, in much the same way of current hand transplants.

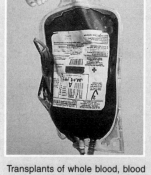

Transplants of whole blood, blood plasma, platelets, and other blood components are crucial to many medical procedures. The donor blood is carefully typed to ensure compatibility with the recipient.

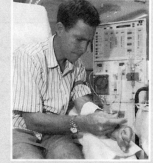

Many patients with kidney failure rely on regular dialysis in order to function. This is expensive and inconvenient, and carries health risks. Such patients are usually waiting for a kidney transplant.

Code: A 2

Xenotransplantation

Chimpanzee

Baboon

Pig

1963 Chimpanzee kidneys were transplanted into 13 patients at Tulane University, Louisianna. One patient survived 9 months.

1964 First cardiac transplant attempted to put the heart of a chimpanzee into a human.

1984 Baby Fae, born with a malformed heart, received a heart from a baboon, and lived only 20 more days.

1992 Liver transplants from baboons to humans, with one patient surviving more than two months. The massive immunosuppression necessary to avoid rejection eventually resulted in a fatal infection.

1995 Jeff Getty received immune cells from a baboon in an attempt to combat his severe AIDS. His condition mysteriously appeared to improve.

1997 Clinical trial using foetal pig nerve cells in patients with Parkinson's disease indicated some success.

Xenotransplantation is an attempt to overcome the shortage of human donor organs by using equivalent organs from other mammals, such as baboons, chimpanzees, and pigs (pig heart valves are in common use). It has not been widely adopted or successful. There is a considerable ethical debate surrounding its use and some justified concern over the possibility of accidentally introducing new diseases into the human population. Known as **zoonoses**, such cross-species infections by viruses have already been observed (e.g. HIV and SARS).

1. Describe three major technical advances that have improved the success rate of organ transplantation:

(a) _____

(b) _____

(c) _____

2. (a) Explain the basis for organ and tissue rejection: _____

(b) Discuss the role of **tissue typing** and **immunosuppressant drugs** in reducing or preventing this response: _____

(c) Describe one of the major undesirable side-effects of using immunosuppressant drugs in transplant recipients: _____

3. Briefly describe the following technologies that are being developed in response to the shortage of donor organs:

(a) Xenotransplantation: _____

(b) Tissue engineering: _____

4. In point form, outline the ethical issues associated with organ and tissue transplants. Consider costs, benefits, source of tissue, and criteria for choosing recipients. If required, debate the issue, or develop your arguments as a separate report: _____

Stem Cells and Tissue Engineering

Cell cultures have been used for many years for medical and research purposes, e.g. for the culture of viruses for vaccine production and in the production of monoclonal antibodies. Reliable techniques in cell culturing have paved the way for new technologies such as **cell replacement therapy** and **tissue engineering**. These technologies require a disease-free and plentiful supply of cells of specific types. Tissue engineering, for example, involves inducing living cells to grow on a scaffold of natural or synthetic material to produce a three-dimensional tissue such as bone or skin. In 1998, an artificial skin called Apligraf became the first product of this type to be approved for

use as a biomedical device. It is now widely used in place of skin grafts. The applications of tissue engineering range from blood vessel replacement and skin, bone, tendon, and cartilage repair, to the treatment of degenerative nerve diseases. A key to the future of this technology will be the developments in **stem cell** research. Stem cells have the ability to develop and form all the tissues of the body. The best source of these is from very early embryos, but some adult tissues (e.g. bone marrow) also contain stem cells. Therapeutic **stem cell cloning** is still in its very early stages and, despite its enormous medical potential, research with human embryonic cells is still banned in some countries.

Engineering a Living Skin

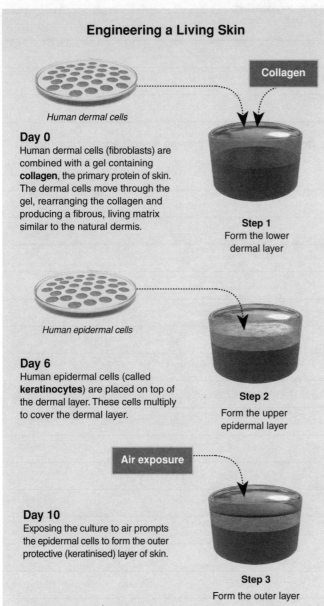

Human dermal cells

Collagen

Day 0
Human dermal cells (fibroblasts) are combined with a gel containing **collagen**, the primary protein of skin. The dermal cells move through the gel, rearranging the collagen and producing a fibrous, living matrix similar to the natural dermis.

Step 1
Form the lower dermal layer

Human epidermal cells

Day 6
Human epidermal cells (called **keratinocytes**) are placed on top of the dermal layer. These cells multiply to cover the dermal layer.

Step 2
Form the upper epidermal layer

Air exposure

Day 10
Exposing the culture to air prompts the epidermal cells to form the outer protective (keratinised) layer of skin.

Step 3
Form the outer layer

Apligraf, produced by the company Organogenesis, was the first living, tissue-engineered skin product to be commercially available. It is used to treat diabetic ulcers and burns, with the patient's own cells and tissues helping to complete the biological repair. Producing Apligraf is a three stage process (above), which results in a bilayered, living structure capable of stimulating wound repair through its own growth factors and proteins. The final size of the Apligraf product is about 75 mm and, from this, tens of . thousands of pieces can be made. The cells used to start the culture are usually obtained from discarded neonatal foreskins collected after circumcision.

The Future? Embryonic Stem Cell Cloning

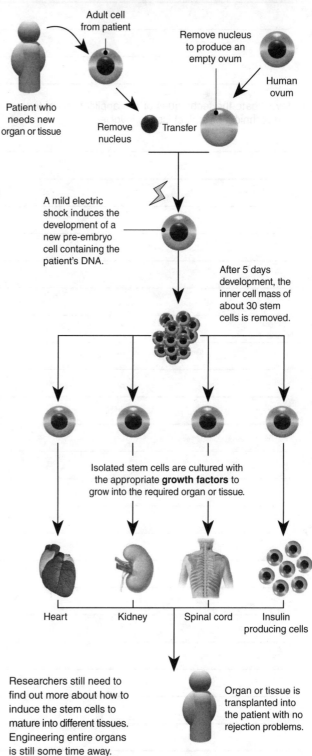

Adult cell from patient

Remove nucleus to produce an empty ovum

Human ovum

Patient who needs new organ or tissue

Remove nucleus

Transfer

A mild electric shock induces the development of a new pre-embryo cell containing the patient's DNA.

After 5 days development, the inner cell mass of about 30 stem cells is removed.

Isolated stem cells are cultured with the appropriate **growth factors** to grow into the required organ or tissue.

Heart   Kidney   Spinal cord   Insulin producing cells

Researchers still need to find out more about how to induce the stem cells to mature into different tissues. Engineering entire organs is still some time away.

Organ or tissue is transplanted into the patient with no rejection problems.

Preventing and Treating Disease

1. Outline the benefits of using an tissue engineered skin product, such as Apligraf, to treat wounds that require grafts:

_____

_____

2. Describe one potential advantage of embryonic stem cell cloning for tissue engineering technology:

_____

_____

3. Discuss the present and potential medical applications of tissue engineering: _____

_____

_____

_____

4. Investigate the techniques or the applications of therapeutic stem cell cloning and prepare a short account discussing the technical or ethical issues involved.

_____

_____

_____

_____

_____

_____

_____

_____

_____

_____

_____

_____

_____

_____

_____

_____

_____

_____

_____

_____

_____

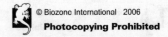

Kidney Dialysis

A dialysis machine is a machine designed to remove wastes from the blood. It is used when the kidneys fail, or when blood acidity, urea, or potassium levels increase much above normal. In kidney dialysis, blood flows through a system of tubes composed of semi-permeable membranes. Dialysis fluid (**dialysate**) has a composition similar to blood except that the concentration of wastes is low. It flows in the opposite direction to the blood on the outside of the dialysis tubes. Consequently, waste products like urea diffuse from the blood into the dialysis fluid, which is constantly replaced. The dialysis fluid flows at a rate of several 100 cm^3 per minute over a large surface area. For some people dialysis is an ongoing procedure, but for others dialysis just allows the kidneys to rest and recover.

Principles of Kidney Dialysis

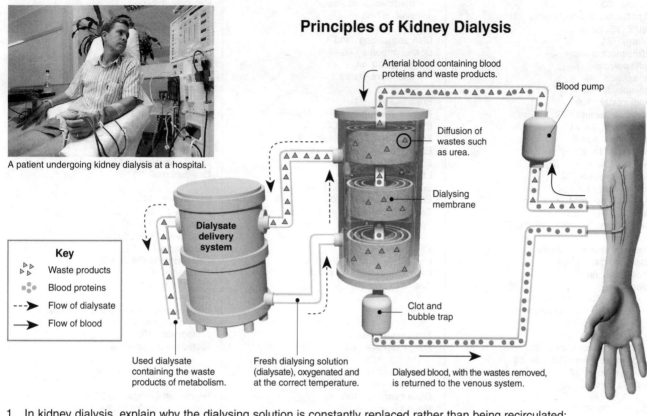

A patient undergoing kidney dialysis at a hospital.

Key
- ▷▷▷ Waste products
- •°• Blood proteins
- ---> Flow of dialysate
- ⟶ Flow of blood

Arterial blood containing blood proteins and waste products.

Blood pump

Diffusion of wastes such as urea.

Dialysing membrane

Dialysate delivery system

Clot and bubble trap

Used dialysate containing the waste products of metabolism.

Fresh dialysing solution (dialysate), oxygenated and at the correct temperature.

Dialysed blood, with the wastes removed, is returned to the venous system.

1. In kidney dialysis, explain why the dialysing solution is constantly replaced rather than being recirculated:

_____

_____

2. Explain why ions such as potassium and sodium, and small molecules such as glucose, do not diffuse rapidly from the blood into the dialysing solution along with the urea:

_____

_____

3. Explain why the urea passes from the blood into the dialysing solution: _____

_____

4. Describe the general transport process involved in dialysis: _____

_____

5. Give a reason why the dialysing solution flows in the opposite direction to the blood: _____

_____

_____

6. Explain why a clot and bubble trap is needed after the blood has been dialysed but before it re-enters the body:

_____

_____

_____

Preventing and Treating Disease

Code: A 2

Index